FOURIER SERIES

P.H. Groenewelt.

sept. 1971.

LIBRARY OF MATHEMATICS

edited by

WALTER LEDERMANN
D.Sc., Ph.D., F.R.S.Ed., Professor of
Mathematics, University of Sussex

FOURIER SERIES

BY

I. N. SNEDDON

LONDON: Routledge & Kegan Paul Ltd
NEW YORK: Dover Publications Inc

First published 1961
by Routledge & Kegan Paul Ltd
Broadway House, 68-74 Carter Lane
London, E.C.4
and in the USA by
Dover Publications Inc
180 Varick Street
New York, 10014

Second impression 1963
Third impression 1966
Fourth impression 1969

SBN 7100 4351 1

Library of Congress Catolog Card Number: 66-21247

Printed in Great Britain by
Latimer Trend & Co Ltd, Plymouth

Preface

THIS book is intended primarily for students of engineering and science who wish to acquire a working knowledge of Fourier series. No attempt is made to develop the theory of Fourier series under wide conditions on the function being represented. The proof of Fourier's fundamental theorem, which is given in Chapter 2, is valid only for a very restrictive class of functions but it covers most of the functions which arise in physical applications. The reader who is interested only in the practical use of Fourier series may omit this chapter, provided he is familiar with the *statement* of the fundamental theorem.

The book begins with an account of the calculations of the Fourier coefficients of a function defined over various finite intervals. In Chapter 3 the principal properties of Fourier series are discussed, again with an emphasis on those properties which are of most interest to physical scientists. The book ends with some simple examples of the applications of Fourier series in the solution of partial differential equations.

It is my pleasant duty to thank Dr. W. Ledermann for the many valuable suggestions he made during the preparation of the manuscript.

I. N. SNEDDON

The University,
Glasgow.

Contents

CONTENTS

CHAPTER ONE

The Fourier Coefficients

---

1. TRIGONOMETRICAL SERIES

By a *trigonometrical series* is meant a series of the type

$$\tfrac{1}{2}a_0 + \sum_{n=1}^{\infty}(a_n \cos nx + b_n \sin nx) \tag{1}$$

where the coefficients $a_0, a_1, \ldots, a_n, \ldots, b_n, \ldots$ do not depend on the real variable x and are themselves supposed to be real.† Except when the series

$$\sum_{n=1}^{\infty}(|a_n| + |b_n|)$$

is convergent it is difficult to establish the convergence of a trigonometrical series, but it is readily seen from equation (1) that if the series does converge to a sum $S(x)$, say, then for every integer r

$$S(x+2r\pi)=S(x),$$

so that we need only study trigonometrical series in an interval of length 2π; for example, we might make it $(-\pi, \pi)$ or $(0, 2\pi)$.

It should be observed that it is sometimes convenient to write (1) in a complex form. If we write $\cos nx = \tfrac{1}{2}(e^{inx} + e^{-inx})$, $\sin nx = \tfrac{1}{2}i(e^{-inx} - e^{inx})$ in equation (1) we obtain the form

$$\sum_{n=-\infty}^{\infty} c_n e^{inx}$$

† The factor $\tfrac{1}{2}$ is added to a_0 for convenience; the reason does not emerge until later.

1

where $c_n = \frac{1}{2}(a_n - ib_n)$, $n > 0$ and $c_{-n} = \bar{c}_n$, the complex conjugate of c_n.

On rare occasions it is possible to sum a trigonometrical series. For example, if

$$S(x) = \sum_{n=1}^{\infty} a^n \sin nx, \quad |a| < 1,$$

then

$$S(x) = \mathscr{I}\left\{\sum_{n=0}^{\infty} (ae^{ix})^n\right\} = \mathscr{I}\left(\frac{1}{1 - ae^{ix}}\right).$$

from which it follows that

$$S(x) = \frac{a \sin x}{1 - 2a \cos x + a^2}$$

2. FOURIER SERIES

The problem which naturally suggests itself is whether it is always possible to represent in $(0, 2\pi)$ a prescribed function by a trigonometrical series. Suppose that a series of the type (1.1) in which $a_0, a_1, \ldots, a_n, \ldots, b_n, \ldots$ are constants, does in fact converge to a sum $f(x)$ so that we may write

$$f(x) = \frac{1}{2}a_0 + \sum_{n=1}^{\infty} (a_n \cos nx + b_n \sin nx). \tag{1}$$

By using elementary properties of the trigonometric functions we can now easily determine a_n, b_n in terms of $f(x)$.

It is readily shown that

$$\int_0^{2\pi} \sin mx \sin nx \, dx = \begin{cases} 0 \text{ if } m \neq n, \\ \pi \text{ if } m = n, \end{cases}$$

and we can write this result neatly by introducing the Kronecker delta δ_{mn} which is 0 if $m \neq n$ and 1 if $m = n$. With this notation we have

$$\int_0^{2\pi} \sin mx \sin nx \, dx = \pi \delta_{mn}. \tag{2}$$

Similarly

$$\int_0^{2\pi} \cos mx \cos nx \, \mathrm{d}x = \pi\delta_{mn}, \quad \int_0^{2\pi} \sin mx \cos nx \, \mathrm{d}x = 0 \qquad (3)$$

and

$$\int_0^{2\pi} \sin nx \, \mathrm{d}x = 0, \quad \int_0^{2\pi} \cos nx \, \mathrm{d}x = 0. \qquad (4)$$

If therefore we multiply both sides of equation (1) by $\cos nx$ and assume that term by term integration with respect to x from 0 to 2π is permissible we find that

$$a_n = \frac{1}{\pi} \int_0^{2\pi} f(x) \cos nx \, \mathrm{d}x \qquad (5a)$$

Similarly, integrating (1) with respect to x and making use of (4), we find that

$$a_0 = \frac{1}{\pi} \int_0^{2\pi} f(x) \, \mathrm{d}x. \qquad (5b)$$

On the other hand if we multiply both sides of equation (1) by $\sin nx$ and integrate with respect to x from 0 to 2π we find that

$$b_n = \frac{1}{\pi} \int_0^{2\pi} f(x) \sin nx \, \mathrm{d}x. \qquad (5c)$$

The coefficients $a_0, a_1, \ldots, a_n, \ldots, b_n, \ldots$ defined by the three equations (5) are called the *Fourier coefficients* of $f(x)$.

This calculation of the Fourier coefficients is based on the assumption that it is known that the trigonometrical series on the right side of equation (1) converges to the value $f(x)$ for all x in $(0, 2\pi)$. Suppose that a function $f(x)$ is defined in $(0, 2\pi)$ and it is such that we can calculate its Fourier coefficients from equations (5). Having calculated the appropriate $a_0, \ldots, a_n, \ldots, b_n, \ldots$ we may write *quite formally*

$$f(x) \sim \tfrac{1}{2}a_0 + \sum_{n=1}^{\infty} (a_n \cos nx + b_n \sin nx). \qquad (6)$$

3

The series on the right of this relation is called *the whole-range Fourier series of $f(x)$*. The symbol $\sim$ has been used in (6) to show that $f(x)$ is not necessarily equal to the series on the right. Indeed the series on the right may be divergent or, if convergent, may converge to some function other than $f(x)$. All that (6) implies is that the f on the left and the $a_0, \ldots, a_n, \ldots, b_n, \ldots$ are connected through the formulae (5a), (5b) and (5c). The theory of Fourier series is concerned with studying the properties of series of the type (6) and in particular in determining the conditions under which the Fourier series equals the function.

The first rigorous proof that, for a general class of functions, the Fourier series, defined as above, does converge to the sum $f(x)$, was given by Dirichlet in 1829. The result of Dirichlet states that if $f(x)$ is defined and bounded in the range $(0, 2\pi)$ and if $f(x)$ satisfies the conditions:

(a) $f(x)$ has only a finite number of maxima and minima;

(b) $f(x)$ has only a finite number of (finite) discontinuities in the range and if, outside the range, $f(x)$ is defined by the relation $f(x+2\pi)=f(x)$ and if a_n and b_n are defined by equations (5a), (5c), then the Fourier series

$$\tfrac{1}{2}a_0 + \sum_{n=1}^{\infty} (a_n \cos nx + b_n \sin nx)$$

converges to the sum

$$\tfrac{1}{2}[f(x+0)+f(x-0)]$$

where $f(x+0)$ is the value of f as we approach x from the right and $f(x-0)$ is the value of f as we approach x from the left (cf. Fig. 1). If $f(x)$ is continuous at the point x this reduces to $f(x)$. The conditions (a), (b) for $f(x)$ are called *Dirichlet's conditions*; we see that they are quite restrictive but Dirichlet's theorem is valid for most of the functions which arise in mathematical physics.

The function $(4-x^2)^{-1}$ does *not* satisfy Dirichlet's conditions in $(0, 2\pi)$ since it has an infinite discontinuity at the point $x=2$ which is in the interval. On the other hand, the

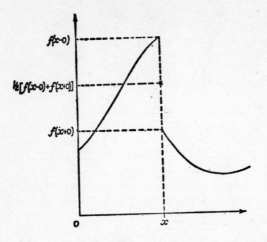

FIG. 1

function $\sin\left(\dfrac{1}{x-1}\right)$ does *not* satisfy Dirichlet's conditions in $(0, 2\pi)$ since it has an infinite number of maxima and minima in the neighbourhood of the point $x=1$. A type of function which occurs in physics and engineering, and

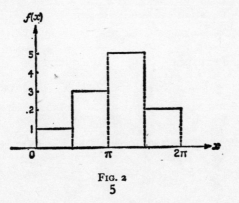

FIG. 2

5

which does satisfy Dirichlet's conditions is the step-function an example of which is shown in Fig. 2. This function, which is defined by the equations

$$f(x) = \begin{cases} 1, & 0 < x < \tfrac{1}{2}\pi, \\ 3, & \tfrac{1}{2}\pi < x < \pi, \\ 5, & \pi < x < \tfrac{3}{2}\pi, \\ 2, & \tfrac{3}{2}\pi < x < 2\pi, \end{cases}$$

has a finite number of finite discontinuities.

We shall postpone the proof of a form of Fourier's theorem (as Dirichlet's result and its variants are known) until the next chapter. Then we shall consider an even simpler class of functions. For the moment we assume the theorem and develop its consequences. We begin with a simple example illustrating the calculation of the Fourier coefficients.

Example I. *Find the whole-range Fourier expansion which represents $f(x)$ for $0 < x < 2\pi$, where*

$$f(x) = \begin{cases} (x-\pi)^2, & \text{for } 0 < x < \pi; \\ \pi^2, & \text{for } \pi < x < 2\pi. \end{cases}$$

Deduce that

$$\text{(i) } \sum_{n=1}^{\infty} \frac{1}{n^2} = \frac{\pi^2}{6}, \quad \text{(ii) } \sum_{n=1}^{\infty} \frac{(-1)^{n-1}}{n^2} = \frac{\pi^2}{12}.$$

From equation (5*b*) we have

$$a_0 = \frac{1}{\pi} \int_0^{2\pi} f(x)\, dx = \frac{1}{\pi} \int_0^{\pi} (x-\pi)^2\, dx + \frac{1}{\pi} \int_\pi^{2\pi} \pi^2\, dx = \frac{4\pi^2}{3}$$

and from equation (5*a*)

$$a_n = \frac{1}{\pi} \int_0^{2\pi} f(x) \cos nx\, dx = \frac{1}{\pi} \int_0^{\pi} (x-\pi)^2 \cos nx\, dx$$
$$+ \frac{1}{\pi} \int_\pi^{2\pi} \pi^2 \cos nx\, dx.$$

The second of the two integrals on the right is zero; the first can be evaluated by integrating by parts (twice). We obtain

6

$$a_n = \frac{2}{n^2}$$

Similarly from equation $(5c)$ we have

$$b_n = \frac{1}{\pi}\int_0^\pi (x-\pi)^2 \sin nx \ \mathrm{d}x + \frac{1}{\pi}\int_\pi^{2\pi} \pi^2 \sin nx \ \mathrm{d}x$$

from which it follows that

$$b_n = \frac{\pi}{n}\cos n\pi - \frac{2}{\pi n^3}(1-\cos n\pi) = \frac{(-1)^n \pi}{n} - \frac{2}{\pi n^3}[1-(-1)^n].$$

Substituting these values in the expression (1) we find that

$$f(x) = \tfrac{2}{3}\pi^2 + 2\sum_{n=1}^\infty \Bigg[\frac{\cos nx}{n^2} +$$

$$\left\{ \frac{(-1)^n \pi}{n} - \frac{2[1-(-1)^n]}{\pi n^3} \right\} \sin nx \Bigg].$$

If we let $x=0$ then, since $f(x)$ is continuous at $x=0$ taking the value π^2 there, it follows that

$$\sum_{n=1}^\infty \frac{1}{n^2} = \frac{\pi^2}{6}.$$

Similarly, if we let $x=\pi$ and note that $f(\pi-0)=0$, $f(\pi+0)=\pi^2$, it follows that

$$\tfrac{1}{2}\pi^2 = \tfrac{2}{3}\pi^2 + 2\sum_{n=1}^\infty \frac{(-1)^n}{n^2}.$$

Therefore

$$\sum_{n=1}^\infty \frac{(-1)^{n+1}}{n^2} = \frac{\pi^2}{12}.$$

3. OTHER TYPES OF WHOLE-RANGE SERIES

We pointed out in section 1 that we could take $(-\pi, \pi)$ to be the range in which to study a trigonometric series of the type (1.1) instead of the range $(0, 2\pi)$. It is obvious that the Fourier series of a function defined in $(-\pi, \pi)$ is of the form (2.6) and that the coefficients are given by equation of the form (2.5a, b, c) with the exception that the limits of integration are now $-\pi$ and π. This result may be established directly, or deduced from that of the last section by a simple change of variable.

In other problems we might wish to find a trigonometric series representing the function $f(x)$ in the interval $(0, 2l)$. If we change the variable from x to ξ where $\xi = \pi x/l$ we see that the function $\phi(\xi) \equiv f(x)$ is defined for $0 \leqslant \xi \leqslant 2\pi$ and

$$\phi(\xi) \sim \tfrac{1}{2}a_0 + \sum_{n=1}^{\infty} (a_n \cos n\xi + b_n \sin n\xi)$$

where

$$a_n = \frac{1}{\pi} \int_0^{2\pi} \phi(\xi) \cos (n\xi) \, \mathrm{d}\xi, \quad b_n = \frac{1}{\pi} \int_0^{2\pi} \phi(\xi) \sin (n\xi) \, \mathrm{d}\xi.$$

Putting $\xi = \pi x/l$ we find that

$$f(x) \sim \tfrac{1}{2}a_0 + \sum_{n=1}^{\infty} \left(a_n \cos \frac{n\pi x}{l} + b_n \sin \frac{n\pi x}{l} \right) \tag{1}$$

where

$$a_n = \frac{1}{l} \int_0^{2l} f(x) \cos \frac{n\pi x}{l} \, \mathrm{d}x, \quad b_n = \frac{1}{l} \int_0^{2l} f(x) \sin \frac{n\pi x}{l} \, \mathrm{d}x. \tag{2}$$

This expansion may also be established directly in an obvious way.

Example 2. *Find the Fourier expansion valid in $(0, 2)$ of the function*

$$f(x) = 4 - x^2.$$

State the value of this series for $x = 0, 1, 2, 10, 11$.

Putting $l = 1$ in equations (1) and (2) above we find that

$$f(x) \sim \tfrac{1}{2}a_0 + \sum_{n=1}^{\infty} \{a_n \cos (n\pi x) + b_n \sin (n\pi x)\}$$

where

$$a_0 = \int_0^2 (4 - x^2) \, \mathrm{d}x = \frac{16}{3},$$

8

$$a_n = \int_0^2 (4-x^2) \cos(n\pi x) \, dx$$

$$= \left[(4-x^2)\frac{\sin(n\pi x)}{n\pi} + \frac{2}{n\pi}\left\{ -\frac{x}{n\pi}\cos(n\pi x) \right\} \right]_0^2$$

$$+ \frac{2}{n^2\pi^2}\int_0^2 \cos(n\pi x) \, dx$$

$$= -\frac{4}{n^2\pi^2},$$

$$b_n = \int_0^2 (4-x^2) \sin(n\pi x) \, dx$$

$$= \left[-(4-x^2)\frac{\cos(n\pi x)}{n\pi} - \frac{2}{n\pi}\left\{ x\frac{\sin(n\pi x)}{n\pi} \right\} \right]_0^2$$

$$+ \frac{2}{n^2\pi^2}\int_0^2 \sin(n\pi x) \, dx$$

$$= \frac{4}{n\pi}.$$

Hence if $0 < x < 2$

$$4-x^2 = S(x) = \frac{8}{3} - \frac{4}{\pi^2}\sum_{n=1}^{\infty}\frac{\cos(n\pi x)}{n^2} + \frac{4}{\pi}\sum_{n=1}^{\infty}\frac{\sin(n\pi x)}{n}$$

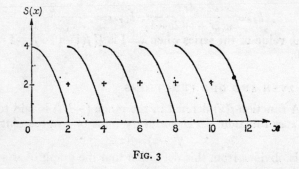

FIG. 3

The graph of the series $S(x)$ is shown in Fig. 3. The

crosses denote that the value $2=\frac{1}{2}[f(2r-0)+f(2r+0)]$ has to be taken. It follows that
$$S(0)=2, \ S(1)=3, \ S(2)=2, \ S(10)=2, \ S(11)=3.$$

If the range is $(-l, l)$ it is easily shown (either directly or by a simple change of variable) that the whole range Fourier expansion is (1) with

$$a_n=\frac{1}{l}\int_{-l}^{l} f(x) \cos\frac{n\pi x}{l} \ dx, \ b_n=\frac{1}{l}\int_{-l}^{l} f(x) \sin\frac{n\pi x}{l} \ dx. \ (3)$$

Example 3. *If $f(x)=1$ for $-1<x<0$ and $f(x)=\cos(\pi x)$ for $0<x<1$, determine the Fourier coefficients of $f(x)$. What is the sum of the series when $x=1$?*

By formulae (3) the Fourier coefficients are

$$a_0=\int_{-1}^{0} dx+\int_{0}^{1} \cos(\pi x) \ dx=1,$$

$$a_n=\int_{-1}^{0} \cos(n\pi x) \ dx+\int_{0}^{1}\cos(n\pi x) \cos(\pi x) \ dx=0,$$

$$b_n=\int_{-1}^{0} \sin(n\pi x) \ dx + \int_{0}^{1}\sin(n\pi x) \cos(\pi x) \ dx$$

$$=\frac{\cos(-n\pi)-1}{n\pi}+\frac{1}{2\pi}\left\{\frac{1-\cos(n+1)\pi}{n+1}+\frac{1-\cos(n-1)\pi}{n-1}\right\}$$

so that

$$b_{2r}=\frac{4r}{\pi(2r+1)(2r-1)}, \ b_{2r+1}=-\frac{2}{\pi(2r+1)}.$$

The value of the series when $x=1$ is $\frac{1}{2}[f(1-0)+f(-1-0)]$ $=0$.

4. EVEN AND ODD FUNCTIONS

A function $f(x)$ defined in the range $(-l, l)$ is said to be an *even* function of x if, for every value of x in the range,

$$f(-x)=f(x). \tag{1}$$

It is obvious from this definition that the graph of an even function is symmetrical with respect to the y-axis. (Cf. Fig. 4(a).)

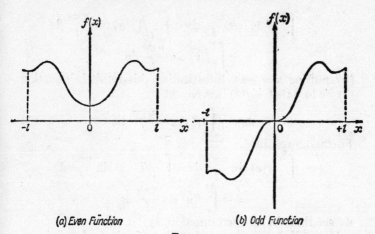

(a) Even Function   (b) Odd Function

FIG. 4

On the other hand, $f(x)$ is said to be *odd* if for all values of x in $(-l, l)$

$$f(-x) = -f(x). \tag{2}$$

It follows immediately from this definition that an odd function will have a graph of the form shown in Fig. 4(b). Also we see that, if the definition (2) is to be consistent, $f(0) = 0$.

We shall now calculate the Fourier coefficients of an even function and those of an odd function.

From equations (2) of §3 we see that the Fourier coefficients may be written

$$a_n = \frac{1}{l} \left\{ \int_0^l f(x) \cos \frac{n\pi x}{l} dx + \int_{-l}^0 f(x) \cos \frac{n\pi x}{l} dx \right\}, \tag{3}$$

$$b_n = \frac{1}{l} \left\{ \int_0^l f(x) \sin \frac{n\pi x}{l} dx + \int_{-l}^0 f(x) \sin \frac{n\pi x}{l} dx \right\}. \tag{4}$$

Now if $f(x)$ is an even function of x it follows from (1) that

11

$$\int_{-l}^{0} f(x) \cos \frac{n\pi x}{l} \, \mathrm{d}x = \int_{-l}^{0} f(-x) \cos \frac{n\pi x}{l} \, \mathrm{d}x$$

$$= \int_{0}^{l} f(u) \cos \frac{n\pi u}{l} \, \mathrm{d}u$$

(by putting $u = -x$). Substituting this result in equation (3) we find that, if $f(x)$ is even

$$a_n = \frac{2}{l} \int_{0}^{l} f(x) \cos \frac{n\pi x}{l} \, \mathrm{d}x. \tag{5}$$

Furthermore, since

$$\int_{-l}^{0} f(x) \sin \frac{n\pi x}{l} \, \mathrm{d}x = \int_{-l}^{0} f(-x) \sin \frac{n\pi x}{l} \, \mathrm{d}x$$

$$= -\int_{0}^{l} f(u) \sin \frac{n\pi u}{l} \, \mathrm{d}u$$

we see that, for an even function, $b_n = 0$.

Hence if $f(x)$ is an *even* function of x in $(-l, l)$ it has a Fourier series of the type

$$\tfrac{1}{2} a_0 + \sum_{n=1}^{\infty} a_n \cos \frac{n\pi x}{l} \tag{6}$$

where the coefficients a_n are given by equation (5).

Suppose now that the function $f(x)$ is odd in $(-l, l)$, then, because of (2)

$$\int_{-l}^{0} f(x) \cos \frac{n\pi x}{l} \, \mathrm{d}x = -\int_{-l}^{0} f(-x) \cos \frac{n\pi x}{l} \, \mathrm{d}x$$

$$= -\int_{0}^{l} f(u) \cos \frac{n\pi u}{l} \, \mathrm{d}u$$

so that the coefficients a_n are all zero. Furthermore, since

$$\int_{-l}^{0} f(x) \sin \frac{n\pi x}{l} \, \mathrm{d}x = -\int_{-l}^{0} f(-x) \sin \frac{n\pi x}{l} \, \mathrm{d}x$$

$$= \int_{0}^{l} f(u) \sin \frac{n\pi u}{l} \, \mathrm{d}u,$$

we find that

$$b_n = \frac{2}{l} \int_{0}^{l} f(x) \sin \frac{n\pi x}{l} \, \mathrm{d}x. \tag{7}$$

Therefore if $f(x)$ is an odd function of x in $(-l, l)$ it has a Fourier series of the form

$$\sum_{n=1}^{\infty} b_n \sin \frac{n\pi x}{l} \tag{8}$$

where the coefficients b_n are calculated from equation (7).

5. HALF-RANGE SINE SERIES

If a function $f(x)$ is defined in the range $(0, l)$ then we may represent it by first extending the definition of $f(x)$ to the range $(-l, l)$ and then constructing the whole-range series of the 'extended' function. For example, we might from $f(x)$ construct the 'odd' function $F(x)$ defined by the equations

$$F(x) = \begin{cases} f(x), & 0 < x < l, \\ -f(-x), & -l < x < 0. \end{cases} \tag{1}$$

From the results of the last section we deduce that, in the range $(0, l)$, we may represent the function $f(x)$ by the sine series

$$f(x) = \sum_{n=1}^{\infty} b_n \sin \frac{n\pi x}{l} \tag{2}$$

where

$$b_n = \frac{2}{l} \int_0^l f(x) \sin \frac{n\pi x}{l} \, dx. \tag{3}$$

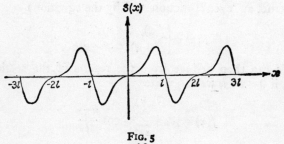

FIG. 5

13

At points outside the range $(0, l)$ the sum of the series (denoted by $S(x)$) may be determined by equation (1) and the periodic property of a trigonometrical series. The relation of $f(x)$ defined in $(0, l)$ to the sum of the series $S(x)$ is illustrated in Fig. 5.

Example 4. *Show that if $0 < x < \pi$,*

$$\cos x = \frac{8}{\pi} \sum_{m=1}^{\infty} \frac{m \sin (2mx)}{4m^2 - 1}.$$

If we represent $\cos x$ by a series of type (2) (with $l = \pi$) we have

$$b_n = \frac{2}{\pi} \int_0^{\pi} \cos x \sin nx \, \mathrm{d}x$$

$$= \frac{1}{\pi} \left\{ \frac{1 - \cos (n+1)\pi}{n+1} + \frac{1 - \cos (n-1)\pi}{n-1} \right\}$$

so that

$$b_{2m+1} = 0, \quad b_{2m} = \frac{8m}{\pi(4m^2 - 1)}$$

and the result follows.

6. HALF-RANGE COSINE SERIES

Instead of extending the function $f(x)$ beyond its range of definition by constructing an 'odd' function we might construct an 'even' function $F(x)$ by the equations

$$F(x) = \begin{cases} f(x), & 0 < x < l, \\ f(-x), & -l < x < 0. \end{cases} \tag{1}$$

We can then deduce from the results of the section 4 that, if $0 < x < l$, we can write

$$f(x) = \tfrac{1}{2}a_0 + \sum_{n=1}^{\infty} a_n \cos \frac{n\pi x}{l} \tag{2}$$

14

where

$$a_n = \frac{2}{l} \int_0^l f(x) \cos \frac{n\pi x}{l} \, dx. \tag{3}$$

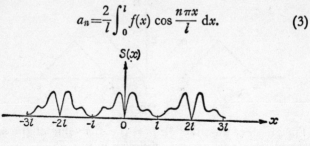

FIG. 6

The value of the sum of the series, $S(x)$, at points outside the range $(0, l)$ in which $f(x)$ is defined, may be determined by equation (1) and the periodic property of the series. The relation between $S(x)$ and $f(x)$ is shown for a simple case in Fig. 6.

Example 5. *Find the half-range cosine series for*

$$f(x) = \begin{cases} 1, & 0 < x < 2 \\ x-2, & 2 < x < 4 \end{cases}$$

for the half-range $0 < x < 4$.

For this function the Fourier cosine coefficients are

$$a_0 = \tfrac{1}{2}\left\{ \int_0^2 x \, dx + \int_2^4 (x-2) \, dx \right\} = 2,$$

$$a_n = \tfrac{1}{2}\left\{ \int_0^2 x \cos \frac{n\pi x}{4} \, dx + \int_2^4 (x-2) \cos \frac{n\pi x}{4} \, dx \right\}$$

$$= \frac{4}{n\pi} \sin\left(\tfrac{1}{2}n\pi\right)\left\{ 1 - \frac{4}{n\pi} \sin\left(\tfrac{1}{2}n\pi\right) \right\}$$

and the required series is

$$S(x) = 1 + \sum_{n=1}^{\infty} a_n \cos\left(\tfrac{1}{4}n\pi x\right) = 1 + \frac{4}{\pi} \sum_{r=1}^{\infty} \frac{(-1)^{r-1}}{2r-1}\left\{ 1 + \frac{4(-1)^r}{(2r-1)\pi} \right\} x$$

$$\cos \frac{(2r-1)\pi x}{4}.$$

15

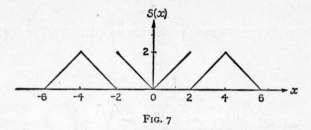

FIG. 7

The graph of the function $S(x)$ (i.e. the value of the series outside the range (0, 4)), is shown in Fig. 7.

7. FOURIER SERIES OVER A GENERAL RANGE (a, b)

Suppose that a function $f(x)$ is defined in the range $a < x < b$. Then the corresponding Fourier series is of the form

$$f(x) = \tfrac{1}{2}A_0 + \sum_{m=1}^{\infty} \left\{ A_m \cos \frac{2m\pi(x-a)}{b-a} + B_m \sin \frac{2m\pi(x-a)}{b-a} \right\}. \quad (1)$$

If we multiply both sides of this equation by $\cos [2m\pi(x-a)/(b-a)]$ and assume that integration with respect to x from a to b is permissible we find that

$$A_m = \frac{2}{b-a} \int_a^b f(x) \cos \frac{2m\pi(x-a)}{b-a} \, dx. \quad (2)$$

Similarly, multiplying both sides of equation (1) by $\sin [2m\pi(x-a)/(b-a)]$ and integrating with respect to x from a to b, we obtain the formula

$$B_m = \frac{2}{b-a} \int_a^b f(x) \sin \frac{2m\pi(x-a)}{b-a} \, dx. \quad (3)$$

From these formulae we can deduce the half-range sine series

$$f(x) = \sum_{m=1}^{\infty} B_m \sin \frac{m\pi(x-a)}{b-a} \quad (4)$$

where B_m is defined by the equation

$$B_m = \frac{2}{b-a} \int_a^b f(x) \sin \frac{m\pi(x-a)}{b-a} \, dx, \qquad (5)$$

and the half-range cosine series

$$f(x) = \tfrac{1}{2} A_0 + \sum_{m=1}^{\infty} A_m \cos \frac{m\pi(x-a)}{b-a}, \qquad (6)$$

with

$$A_m = \frac{2}{b-a} \int_a^b f(x) \cos \frac{m\pi(x-a)}{b-a} \, dx. \qquad (7)$$

These forms of Fourier series can be derived from that for the interval $(0, 2\pi)$ by change of origin and change in unit of length on the x-axis. The conditions for convergence etc. are the same in all cases.

8. ORTHONORMAL SETS OF FUNCTIONS

If a set of functions $\phi_1(x)$, $\phi_2(x)$, $\phi_3(x)$, ... defined over the interval (a, b) has the property that

$$\int_a^b \phi_m(x) \, \phi_n(x) \, dx = \delta_{m,n} \qquad (1)$$

where $\delta_{m,n}$ denotes the Kronecker delta, we say that the set is *orthonormal*. The set is said to be *complete* if the conditions $\int \psi \phi_n \, dx = 0 (n = 1, 2, \ldots)$ imply that $\psi(x) \equiv 0$.

Assuming that an arbitrary function $f(x)$ defined over the interval (a, b) can be expanded in terms of the complete set of orthonormal functions ϕ_1, ϕ_2, ..., in the form

$$f(x) = \sum_{n=1}^{\infty} a_n \, \phi_n(x) \qquad (2)$$

we can determine the values of the coefficients a_1, a_2, ..., by a method analogous to that used to determine the Fourier coefficients. If we multiply both sides of equation

17

(2) by $\phi_m(x)$ and integrate with respect to x from a to b we find that

$$\int_a^b f(x)\phi_m(x)\,\mathrm{d}x = \sum_{n=1}^{\infty} a_n \int_a^b \phi_m(x)\,\phi_n(x)\,\mathrm{d}x$$

$$= \sum_{n=1}^{\infty} a_n\,\delta_{m,n}$$

$$= a_m.$$

Hence if we write

$$(f,\ \phi_n) = \int_a^b f(x)\phi_n(x)\,\mathrm{d}x \tag{3}$$

we see by substituting in equation (2) that

$$f(x) = \Sigma\,(f,\ \phi_n)\,\phi_n(x). \tag{4}$$

It will be observed that $(f,\ \phi_n)$ is a number.

The formula (4) is the analogue of the formula

$$\mathbf{v} = (\mathbf{v}.\mathbf{i})\mathbf{i} + (\mathbf{v}.\mathbf{j})\mathbf{j} + (\mathbf{v}.\mathbf{k})\mathbf{k}$$

in ordinary vector calculus which enables us to express any arbitrary vector in terms of three orthogonal base vectors $\mathbf{i}, \mathbf{j}, \mathbf{k}$.

It is easily shown by elementary integrations that the set of functions

$$\phi_n(x) = \sqrt{\frac{2}{l}} \sin \frac{n\pi x}{l}$$

$n = 1, 2, 3, \ldots$ form an orthonormal set in the interval $(0, l)$.

EXERCISES ON CHAPTER I

1. Expand $f(x)$ in a Fourier series in the interval $(0, 2\pi)$, if
$$f(x) = \begin{cases} -\pi, & 0 < x < \pi, \\ x - \pi, & \pi < x < 2\pi. \end{cases}$$
State the value the series takes at $x = \pi$ and hence show that
$$\sum_{r=0}^{\infty} \frac{1}{(2r+1)^2} = \frac{\pi^2}{8}.$$

2. Prove that, if

$$f(x) = \begin{cases} \sin \tfrac{1}{2}x, & 0 \leqslant x < \pi, \\ -\sin \tfrac{1}{2}x, & \pi < x \leqslant 2\pi, \end{cases}$$

then, for $0 \leqslant x \leqslant 2\pi$, $x \neq \pi$,

$$f(x) = \frac{8}{\pi} \sum_{n=1}^{\infty} (-1)^{n-1} \frac{n \sin nx}{4n^2 - 1}.$$

Deduce that

$$\sum_{n=1}^{\infty} (-1)^{r-1} \frac{r - \tfrac{1}{2}}{r^2 - r + \tfrac{3}{16}} = \frac{\pi}{\sqrt{2}}.$$

3. Find the Fourier series of the function $f(x)$ where

$$f(x) = \begin{cases} \cos x & \text{for } -\pi < x < 0, \\ -\cos x & \text{for } 0 < x < \pi, \end{cases}$$

and deduce that

$$\sum_{n=1}^{\infty} (-1)^{n-1} \frac{2n - 1}{(4n-1)(4n-3)} = \frac{\pi}{8\sqrt{2}}.$$

4. Obtain the Fourier series of the function $f(x)$, defined for all values of x by the equations:
  (i) $f(x) = e^x$, $-\pi < x \leqslant \pi$,
  (ii) $f(x + 2\pi) = f(x)$, for all values of x.
Deduce that

$$\sum_{n=1}^{\infty} \frac{1}{n^2 + 1} = \tfrac{1}{2}(\pi \coth \pi - 1).$$

5. Find the half-range Fourier cosine series which represents the function $\cos \lambda x$ for values of x between 0 and π, where λ is not an integer.

Hence show that, when λ is not an integer,

  (i) $\pi \cot \pi \lambda = \dfrac{1}{\lambda} + \sum_{n=1}^{\infty} \dfrac{2\lambda}{\lambda^2 - n^2}$;

  (ii) $\pi \operatorname{cosec} \pi \lambda = \sum_{n=1}^{\infty} (-1)^n \left(\dfrac{1}{n+\lambda} + \dfrac{1}{n-1-\lambda} \right).$

6. Show that

  (i) $\pi^2 - x^2 = \dfrac{2}{3}\pi^2 + 4(\cos x - \tfrac{1}{4}\cos 2x + \tfrac{1}{9}\cos 3x - \dots)$

where $-\pi \leqslant x \leqslant \pi$, and that

  (ii) $x = \dfrac{1}{2}\pi - \dfrac{4}{\pi}\left(\cos x + \dfrac{1}{3^2}\cos 3x + \dfrac{1}{5^2}\cos 5x + \dots \right)$

for $0 \leqslant x \leqslant \pi$. Deduce that

$$\frac{1}{1^2} + \frac{1}{3^2} + \frac{1}{5^2} + \dots = \frac{\pi^2}{8},$$

and that

$$\frac{1}{1^2} - \frac{1}{2^2} + \frac{1}{3^2} - \frac{1}{4^2} + \frac{1}{5^2} + \dots = \frac{\pi^2}{12}.$$

CHAPTER TWO

A Proof of Fourier's Theorem†

---

1. PIECEWISE-CONTINUOUS FUNCTIONS

In this chapter we shall give a simple proof of Fourier's theorem; that is, we shall set up sufficient conditions on the function $f(x)$ for the series

$$\tfrac{1}{2}a_0 + \sum_{n=1}^{\infty} (a_n \cos nx + b_n \sin nx) \qquad (1)$$

in which

$$a_n = \frac{1}{\pi} \int_0^{2\pi} f(x) \cos nx \, \mathrm{d}x, \quad b_n = \frac{1}{\pi} \int_0^{2\pi} f(x) \sin nx \, \mathrm{d}x \qquad (2)$$

to represent the function $f(x)$ in the interval $(0, 2\pi)$.

In this section we consider the class of functions with which we shall deal in our form of the proof of Fourier's theorem.

A function $\psi(x)$ is said to be *piecewise-continuous* in a finite interval (a, b) if:

(i) the interval (a, b) can be subdivided into a finite number, m say, of intervals, (a, a_1), (a_1, a_2), ..., (a_r, a_{r+1}), ..., (a_{m-1}, b), in each of which $f(x)$ is continuous;

(ii) $f(x)$ is finite at the end-points of such an interval.

To express the condition (ii) succinctly we introduce a special notation. If $h \to 0$ purely through positive values of h, we say that $\psi(x+h) \to \psi(x+0)$, whenever the limit exists.

† A reader interested only in the practical use of Fourier series may omit this chapter provided he is familiar with the statement of the theorem at the end of the chapter.

Similarly, if $h \to 0$ through negative values of h only, we say that $\psi(x+h) \to \psi(x-0)$. For $\psi(0+0)$ we shall write $\psi(+0)$ and for $\psi(0-0)$ we shall write $\psi(-0)$. Condition (ii) then states that at each end-point a_r of an interval $f(a_r+0)$ and $f(a_r-0)$ should both be finite (though they need not be equal). Because of condition (ii) and the continuity of $f(x)$ in (a_r, a_{r+1}) we see that $f(x)$ is bounded in that interval so that

$$|\psi(x)| < M_{r+1} \text{ for } a_r \leqslant x \leqslant a_{r+1} \tag{3}$$

and since the number of intervals m is finite this implies that

$$|\psi(x)| < M \text{ for } a \leqslant x \leqslant b, \tag{4}$$

where M is the greatest of the numbers $M_1, M_2, \ldots, M_m$.

Furthermore the integral

$$\int_a^b \psi(x) \mathrm{d}x$$

is finite being the sum

$$\sum_{r=0}^{m-1} \int_{a_r}^{a_{r+1}} \psi(x) \, \mathrm{d}x \tag{5}$$

of a finite number of integrals of continuous functions.

Another concept we require is that of a right-hand derivative. If the limit

$$\lim_{h \to 0} \frac{f(\xi+h) - f(\xi+0)}{h}$$

in which $h \to 0$ through *positive* values of h, has a finite value we say that $f(x)$ possesses a *right-hand derivative* at the point $x = \xi$. Similarly if the limit

$$\lim_{h \to 0} \frac{f(\xi+h) - f(\xi-0)}{h}$$

exists when $h \to 0$ through *negative* values of h we say that $f(x)$ possesses a *left-hand derivative* at the point $x = \xi$. The geometrical interpretation of these concepts is obvious. In Fig. 8 if ϕ_1 and ϕ_2 are the angles made by the tangents to

21

the two branches of the curve $y=f(x)$ at the point $x=\xi$, then $\tan \phi_1$ is the value of the right-hand derivative and $\tan \phi_2$ is the value of the left-hand derivative.

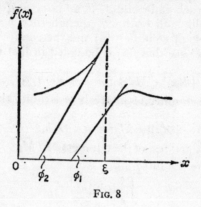

FIG. 8

2. SOME IMPORTANT LIMITS

Before proceeding to the proof of our form of Fourier's theorem, we shall prove some preliminary results concerning the behaviour as $N \to \infty$ of certain integrals whose integrands have a factor of the kind $\sin (Nu)$

Lemma 1. *If $\psi(u)$ is piecewise continuous in the interval $a \leqslant u \leqslant b$, then*

$$\lim_{N \to \infty} \int_a^b \psi(u) \sin (Nu)\, du = 0. \tag{1}$$

The proof in the general case is difficult; we shall assume in addition that $\psi'(u)$ is piecewise continous.

If we divide the interval (a, b) into m intervals of the type described in the last section, then, using the expression (5) of that section for the integral,

$$\int_a^b \psi(u) \sin Nu\, du = \sum_{r=0}^{m-1} \int_{a_r}^{a_{r+1}} \psi(u) \sin Nu\, du$$

22

$$\int_{a_r}^{a_{r+1}} \psi(u) \sin Nu \ du = \left[-\psi(u) \frac{\cos Nu}{N} \right]_{a_r}^{a_{r+1}}$$
$$+ \frac{1}{N} \int_{a_r}^{a_{r+1}} \psi'(u) \cos Nu \ du.$$

The last integral is bounded so that the whole expression is less than M_r/N where M_r is finite. If M is the greatest of the finite numbers $1M_01, 1M_11, \ldots, 1M_{m-1}1$ we have

$$1 \int_a^b \psi(u) \sin Nu \ du 1 < \frac{Mm}{N}$$

Since M, m are finite this tends to zero as $N \to \infty$ and the lemma is proved.

Lemma 2. *If $\psi(u)$ and $\psi'(u)$ are piecewise-continuous in the interval $0 < u \leqslant a$ and ψ has a right-hand derivative at $u = 0$, then*

$$\lim_{N \to \infty} \int_0^a \psi(u) \frac{\sin Nu}{u} \ du = \tfrac{1}{2}\pi\psi(+0). \tag{2}$$

From the identity

$$\psi(u) = \psi(+0) + [\psi(u) - \psi(+0)] \tag{3}$$

we find that

$$\int_0^a \psi(u) \frac{\sin Nu}{u} \ du = \psi(+0) \int_0^a \frac{\sin Nu}{u}$$
$$+ \int_0^a \phi(u) \sin Nu \ du \tag{4}$$

where

$$\phi(u) = \frac{\psi(u) - \psi(+0)}{u}. \tag{5}$$

Now, making the substitution $\xi = Nu$, we find that

$$\int_0^a \frac{\sin Nu}{u} \ du = \int_0^{Na} \frac{\sin \xi}{\xi} \ d\xi \to \int_0^\infty \frac{\sin \xi}{\xi} \ d\xi = \tfrac{1}{2}\pi.\dagger$$

Since $\psi(u)$ is piecewise-continuous in $0 \leqslant u \leqslant a$, it follows that the function $\phi(u) = [\psi(u) - \psi(+0)]/u$ is piecewise-

† For a proof that $\int_0^\infty \xi^{-1} \sin \xi \ d\xi = \tfrac{1}{2}\pi$, see R. P. Gillespie, *Integration* (Oliver and Boyd, 1939), p. 83.

23

continuous in $0 < u \leqslant a$. Furthermore, since $\psi(u)$ has a right-hand derivative at $u=0$ it follows that $\phi(+0)$ exists. Hence $\phi(u)$ is piecewise-continuous in $0 \leqslant u \leqslant a$, and from lemma 1, it follows that

$$\lim_{N \to \infty} \int_0^a \phi(u) \sin Nu \, \mathrm{d}u = 0.$$

Letting $N \to \infty$ in equation (4), we obtain equation (2).

Lemma 3. *If $\psi(u)$ and $\psi'(u)$ are piecewise-continuous in the interval $a < u < b$ and ψ has right and left derivatives at a point $u=x$, where $a < x < b$, then*

$$\lim_{N \to \infty} \int_a^b \psi(u) \frac{\sin N(u-x)}{u-x} \, \mathrm{d}u = \tfrac{1}{2}\pi[\psi(x+0) + \psi(x-0)]. \quad (6)$$

We divide the interval (a, b) into two parts (a, x), (x, b).

$$\int_a^b \psi(u) \frac{\sin N(u-x)}{u-x} \, \mathrm{d}u = \int_a^x \psi(u) \frac{\sin N(u-x)}{u-x} \, \mathrm{d}u$$
$$+ \int_x^b \psi(u) \frac{\sin N(u-x)}{u-x} \, \mathrm{d}u.$$

Now by the change of variable $u = x - \xi$ we find that

$$\int_a^x \psi(u) \frac{\sin N(u-x)}{u-x} \, \mathrm{d}u = \int_0^{x-a} \phi(\xi) \frac{\sin N\xi}{\xi} \, \mathrm{d}\xi$$

where $\phi(\xi) = \psi(x-\xi)$ and by lemma 2, this integral tends to $\tfrac{1}{2}\pi\phi(+0)$, i.e. to $\tfrac{1}{2}\pi\psi(x-0)$. Similarly putting $u = x + \eta$, we find that

$$\int_x^b \psi(u) \frac{\sin N(u-x)}{u-x} \, \mathrm{d}u = \int_0^{b-x} \chi(\eta) \sin N\eta \, \frac{\mathrm{d}\eta}{\eta}$$

where $\chi(\eta) = \psi(x+\eta)$. By lemma 2, this integral tends to $\tfrac{1}{2}\pi\chi(+0)$, i.e. to $\tfrac{1}{2}\pi\psi(x+0)$. Adding the two limits we obtain equation (6).

3. A FOURIER THEOREM

We shall now make use of the lemmas we established in the last section to establish a proof of Fourier's theorem. Here we prove the theorem for functions which are piecewise-continuous in the interval $(0, 2\pi)$ and have right- and left-hand derivatives at every point. Such functions will be called 'piecewise-smooth'. It is readily shown that this condition is not necessary for the validity of the theorem, but it is not easy to give more general conditions without going deeply into certain analytical questions.†

We consider the sum of the first $2N+1$ terms of the Fourier series

$$S_N(x) = \tfrac{1}{2}a_0 + \sum_{n=1}^{N} (a_n \cos nx + b_n \sin nx) \tag{1}$$

in which the Fourier coefficients a_n, b_n are given by the integral formulae

$$a_n = \frac{1}{\pi} \int_0^{2\pi} f(u) \cos nu \, \mathrm{d}u, \quad b_n = \frac{1}{\pi} \int_0^{2\pi} f(u) \sin nu \, \mathrm{d}u. \tag{2}$$

Substituting from equations (2) into equation (1), and interchanging the order of the summation and the integration we find that

$$S_N(x) = \frac{1}{\pi} \int_0^{2\pi} f(u) \left\{ \tfrac{1}{2} + \sum_{n=1}^{N} (\cos nx \cos nu + \sin nx \sin nu) \right\} \mathrm{d}u.$$

Now

$$\tfrac{1}{2} + \sum_{n=1}^{N} (\cos nx \cos nu + \sin nx \sin nu) = \frac{\sin[(N+\tfrac{1}{2})(u-x)]}{2 \sin[\tfrac{1}{2}(u-x)]}$$

so that

$$S_N(x) = \int_0^{2\pi} \psi(u) \frac{\sin [(N+\tfrac{1}{2})(u-x)]}{u-x} \, \mathrm{d}u, \tag{3}$$

where

$$\psi(u) = \frac{1}{\pi} f(u) \frac{\tfrac{1}{2}(u-x)}{\sin \tfrac{1}{2}(u-x)}. \tag{4}$$

† For a full discussion of these questions the reader is referred to E. C. Titchmarsh, *The Theory of Functions* (Oxford, 1932), Chapter XIII, or G. H. Hardy and W. W. Rogosinski, *Fourier Series* (Cambridge, 1944).

If $f(u)$ is piecewise-continuous in the interval $(0, 2\pi)$ and has right- and left-hand derivatives at the point $u=x$, then so is $\psi(u)$ and by lemma **3**,

$$\lim_{N\to\infty} S_N(x) = \tfrac{1}{2}\pi[\psi(x+0)+\psi(x-0)].$$

Now

$$\psi(x+0) = \frac{1}{\pi}f(x+0)\lim_{u\to x}\frac{\tfrac{1}{2}(u-x)}{\sin\tfrac{1}{2}(u-x)} = \frac{1}{\pi}f(x+0),$$

and similarly $\psi(x-0)=\dfrac{1}{\pi}f(x-0)$. Hence

$$\lim_{N\to\infty} S_N(x) = \tfrac{1}{2}[f(x+0)+f(x-0)]$$

Hence we have proved:

Theorem 1.

If $f(x)$ is periodic with period 2π, i.e. if $f(x+2\pi)=f(x)$, for all values of x, and if $f(x)$ is piecewise-smooth in the interval $(0, 2\pi)$, the Fourier series

$$\tfrac{1}{2}a_0 + \sum_{n=1}^{\infty}(a_n\cos nx + b_n\sin nx)$$

in which the coefficients are given by the formulae

$$a_n = \frac{1}{\pi}\int_0^{2\pi}f(u)\cos nu\,du,\ b_n = \frac{1}{\pi}\int_0^{2\pi}f(u)\sin nu\,du,\ (n=0, 1, 2,...),$$

converges to the sum

$$\tfrac{1}{2}[f(x+0)+f(x-0)]$$

at each point of the interval.

EXERCISES ON CHAPTER II

1. Show that, if $0 < \theta < 2\pi$,

$$\sum_{n=-m}^{m} \frac{\sin (n+\alpha)\theta}{n+\alpha} = \int_{0}^{\theta} \cos (\alpha\theta) \frac{\sin (m+\tfrac{1}{2})\theta \; d\theta}{\sin \tfrac{1}{2}\theta},$$

and find the sum of the series

$$\sum_{-\infty}^{\infty} \frac{\sin (n+\alpha)\theta}{n+\alpha}$$

when $0 < \theta < 2\pi$. Deduce that, if α is not an integer,

$$\sum_{n=1}^{\infty} \frac{(-1)^n}{\alpha^2 - n^2} = \frac{1}{2\alpha^2} (\pi\alpha \operatorname{cosec} \pi\alpha - 1).$$

2. Prove that, if $0 < \theta < 2\pi$,

$$\sum_{n=-m}^{m} \frac{1 - \cos (n+\alpha)\theta}{n+\alpha} = \int_{0}^{\theta} \sin (\alpha u) \frac{\sin (m+\tfrac{1}{2})u}{\sin \tfrac{1}{2}u} \; du$$

and deduce that, if $0 < \theta < 2\pi$ and α is not an integer,

(i) $\dfrac{1}{\alpha} + \sum_{n=1}^{\infty} \dfrac{2\alpha}{\alpha^2 - n^2} = \sum_{n=-\infty}^{\infty} \dfrac{\cos (n+\alpha)\theta}{n+\alpha},$

(ii) $\dfrac{1}{\alpha} + \sum_{n=1}^{\infty} \dfrac{2\alpha}{\alpha^2 - n^2} = \pi \cot \pi\alpha.$

CHAPTER THREE

Properties of Fourier Series

1. INTEGRATION OF FOURIER SERIES

In this chapter we shall consider further properties of Fourier series principally the integration and differentiation of such series. We shall begin with the integration of Fourier Series.

Suppose that $a_0, a_1, \ldots, b_1, \ldots$ are the Fourier coefficients of a function $f(x)$ defined in the interval $(-\pi, \pi)$. If $f(x)$ satisfies Dirichlet's conditions in $(-\pi, \pi)$ (see p. 4 above) then the function

$$F(x) = \int_{-\pi}^{x} f(t) \, dt - \tfrac{1}{2}a_0 x \qquad (1)$$

is continuous in that interval and it is readily seen that the other conditions of Theorem **1** are satisfied and that

$$F(\pi) = F(-\pi) = \tfrac{1}{2}a_0 \pi$$

It follows from Theorem **1** that for all x in the closed interval $(-\pi, \pi)$

$$F(x) = \tfrac{1}{2}A_0 + \sum_{n=1}^{\infty} (A_n \cos nx + B_n \sin nx),$$

where the coefficients A_n and B_n are defined by the relations

$$A_n = \frac{1}{\pi} \int_{-\pi}^{\pi} F(x) \cos nx \, dx, \quad B_n = \frac{1}{\pi} \int_{-\pi}^{\pi} F(x) \sin nx \, dx.$$

Integrating by parts we find that, if $n \geqslant 1$,

$$A_n = \frac{1}{\pi} \left[\frac{\sin nx}{n} F(x) \right]_{-\pi}^{\pi} - \frac{1}{n\pi} \int_{-\pi}^{\pi} F'(x) \sin nx \, dx.$$

Now
$$F'(x) = f(x) - \tfrac{1}{2}a_0$$
so that
$$A_n = -\frac{1}{n\pi}\int_{-\pi}^{\pi} f(x)\sin(nx)\,\mathrm{d}x = -\frac{b_n}{n}.$$

In a similar way we can show that
$$B_n = \frac{a_n}{n}.$$

We therefore obtain the Fourier series
$$F(x) = \tfrac{1}{2}A_0 + \sum_{n=1}^{\infty}\left(-\frac{b_n}{n}\cos nx + \frac{a_n}{n}\sin nx\right). \qquad (2)$$

Now $\tfrac{1}{2}[F(\pi-0)+F(-\pi+0)] = \tfrac{1}{2}a_0\pi$ so that putting $x = \pi$ in this equation we find that
$$\tfrac{1}{2}a_0\pi = \tfrac{1}{2}A_0 - \sum_{n=1}^{\infty}\frac{b_n}{n}\cos n\pi. \qquad (3)$$

If we eliminate A_0 from equations (2) and (3) and substitute for $F(x)$ from equation (1) we find that if $-\pi \leqslant x \leqslant \pi$
$$\int_{-\pi}^{x} f(u)\mathrm{d}u = \tfrac{1}{2}a_0(x+\pi) + \sum_{n=1}^{\infty}\frac{1}{n}[b_n(\cos n\pi - \cos nx) + a_n\sin nx] \qquad (4)$$

Similarly if $-\pi \leqslant \xi \leqslant \pi$
$$\int_{-\pi}^{\xi} f(u)\mathrm{d}u = \tfrac{1}{2}a_0(\xi+\pi) + \sum_{n=1}^{\infty}\frac{1}{n}[b_n(\cos n\pi - \cos n\xi) + a_n\sin n\xi] \qquad (5)$$

Subtracting (5) from (4) we find that if $-\pi \leqslant \xi < x \leqslant \pi$ then
$$\int_{\xi}^{x} f(u)\mathrm{d}u = \tfrac{1}{2}a_0(x-\xi) + \sum_{n=1}^{\infty}\frac{1}{n}[b_n(\cos n\xi - \cos nx) + a_n(\sin nx$$
$$-\sin n\xi)]. \quad (6)$$

Hence we obtain

Theorem 2.

If $f(x)$ satisfies Dirichlet's conditions in the interval $(-\pi, \pi)$ and if a_n, b_n are the Fourier coefficients of $f(x)$ then

$$\int_{\xi}^{x} f(x) \, dx = \tfrac{1}{2}a_0(x-\xi) + \sum_{n=1}^{\infty} \frac{1}{n}[b_n(\cos n\xi - \cos nx) + a_n(\sin nx - \sin n\xi)],$$

when $-\pi \leqslant \xi < x \leqslant \pi$.

It will be observed that the series (6) is obtained by integrating the Fourier series for $f(x)$ term by term. Furthermore, the series (6) will not be a Fourier series unless $a_0 = 0$.

Example. *Find the Fourier series of the function defined by the formulae*

$$f(x) = \begin{cases} 1, & 0 < x < \pi, \\ -1, & -\pi < x < 0, \end{cases}$$

and deduce that

$$\frac{1}{1^2} + \frac{1}{3^2} + \frac{1}{5^2} + \ldots = \frac{\pi^2}{8}.$$

Since $f(x)$ is an *odd* function of x all the a_n's are zero and the b_n's are given by the formula

$$b_n = \frac{2}{\pi}\int_{0}^{\pi} \sin nx \, dx = \frac{2}{n\pi}(1 - \cos n\pi)$$

so that

$$f(x) \sim \frac{4}{\pi}\sum_{r=1}^{\infty} \frac{\sin(2r-1)x}{2r-1}.$$

From Theorem 2

$$\int_{0}^{\frac{1}{2}\pi} f(x) \, dx = \frac{4}{\pi}\sum_{r=1}^{\infty} \frac{1}{(2r-1)^2}.$$

Now

$$\int_{0}^{\frac{1}{2}\pi} f(x) \, dx = \int_{0}^{\frac{1}{2}\pi} 1 \cdot dx = \tfrac{1}{2}\pi$$

showing that

$$\sum_{r=1}^{\infty} \frac{1}{(2r-1)^2} = \frac{\pi^2}{8}.$$

It is readily shown that the other forms of Fourier series can be integrated term by term in like circumstances.

2. PARSEVAL'S THEOREM

Closely related to the theorem of the last section is a theorem due to Parseval. We shall not give a rigorous proof but merely show its plausibility. If $f(x)$ and $g(x)$ are continuous in $(-\pi, \pi)$ and have the Fourier expansions

$$f(x) = \tfrac{1}{2}a_0 + \sum_{n=1}^{\infty} (a_n \cos nx + b_n \sin nx),$$

$$g(x) = \tfrac{1}{2}\alpha_0 + \sum_{n=1}^{\infty} (\alpha_n \cos nx + \beta_n \sin nx)$$

then

$$f(x)g(x) = \tfrac{1}{2}a_0 g(x) + \sum_{n=1}^{\infty} [a_n g(x) \cos nx + b_n g(x) \sin nx].$$

If we now integrate with respect to x from $-\pi$ to π and make use of the formulae for the Fourier coefficients of $g(x)$ we obtain

Theorem 3.

If $f(x)$ and $g(x)$ are continuous in $(-\pi, \pi)$ and a_n, b_n are the Fourier coefficients of $f(x)$, α_n, β_n those of $g(x)$ then

$$\int_{-\pi}^{\pi} f(x)g(x)\,\mathrm{d}x = \tfrac{1}{2}\pi a_0 \alpha_0 + \pi \sum_{n=1}^{\infty} (a_n \alpha_n + b_n \beta_n). \quad (1)$$

In particular if we take $g(x) = f(x)$ we obtain

31

Theorem 4. (*Parseval's Theorem.*)

If $f(x)$ is continuous in the range $(-\pi, \pi)$ and has Fourier coefficients a_n, b_n then

$$\int_{-\pi}^{\pi} [f(x)]^2 \, \mathrm{d}x = \tfrac{1}{2}\pi a_0^2 + \pi \sum_{n=1}^{\infty} (a_n^2 + b_n^2). \tag{2}$$

Example. *Find the Fourier series of the function $f(x)$ defined by the equations*

$$f(x) = \begin{cases} -x, & -\pi \leqslant x \leqslant 0, \\ x, & 0 \leqslant x \leqslant \pi, \end{cases}$$

and deduce that

$$\frac{1}{1^4} + \frac{1}{3^4} + \frac{1}{5^4} + \dots = \frac{\pi^4}{96}.$$

For the function $f(x)$ we have the Fourier coefficients

$$a_0 = \pi, \quad a_n = \frac{2}{\pi n^2}[\cos(n\pi) - 1], \quad b_n = 0,$$

so that

$$f(x) = \tfrac{1}{2}\pi - \frac{4}{\pi} \sum_{r=1}^{\infty} \frac{\cos(2r-1)\pi}{(2r-1)^2}.$$

Hence from equation (2) we have that

$$\int_{-\pi}^{\pi} x^2 \, \mathrm{d}x = \tfrac{1}{2}\pi \cdot \pi^2 + \pi \cdot \frac{16}{\pi^2} \sum_{r=1}^{\infty} \frac{1}{(2r-1)^4}$$

from which the stated result follows.

We get an important special case of Theorem **3** by taking

$$g(x) = x, \quad -\pi \leqslant x < \pi$$

for which

$$\alpha_n = 0, \quad \beta_n = -\frac{2}{n}\cos n\pi = \frac{2(-1)^{n-1}}{n}. \tag{3}$$

Substituting from (3) into (1) we obtain the formula

$$\frac{1}{2\pi}\int_{-\pi}^{\pi} xf(x)\ \mathrm{d}x = \sum_{n=1}^{\infty}(-1)^{n-1}\frac{b_n}{n} \qquad (4)$$

where b_n are the Fourier sine coefficients of $f(x)$ in the range $(-\pi, \pi)$.

3. THE ROOT-MEAN-SQUARE VALUE OF A PERIODIC FUNCTION

If $f(t)$ is a periodic function with period T, so that

$$f(t+rT)=f(t), \qquad (1)$$

for all integral values of r, then $f(t)$ can, in general, be represented by a Fourier series of the type

$$f(t)=\tfrac{1}{2}a_0 + \sum_{n=1}^{\infty}\left(a_n \cos\frac{2\pi nt}{T}+b_n \sin\frac{2\pi nt}{T}\right). \qquad (2)$$

Since

$$\int_0^{nT} f(t)\ \mathrm{d}t = n\int_0^{T} f(t)\ \mathrm{d}t$$

it follows that the mean value of the function taken over n complete periods is

$$\bar{f}=\frac{1}{nT}\int_0^{nT} f(t)\ \mathrm{d}t = \frac{1}{T}\int_0^{T} f(t)\ \mathrm{d}t. \qquad (3)$$

Substituting from (2) into (3) and using the results

$$\int_0^{T}\mathrm{d}t = T, \quad \int_0^{T}\sin\frac{2\pi nt}{T}\ \mathrm{d}t = \int_0^{T}\cos\frac{2\pi nt}{T}\ \mathrm{d}t = 0,$$

we find that

$$\bar{f}=\tfrac{1}{2}a_0 \qquad (4)$$

so that we can rewrite equation (2) in the form

$$f(t)=\bar{f} + \sum_{n=1}^{\infty}\left(a_n \cos\frac{2\pi nt}{T}+b_n \sin\frac{2\pi nt}{T}\right). \qquad (5)$$

It is obvious from equation (4) that the mean value of a function does not have much significance for a periodic function. More information is given by the *root-mean-square value* which is defined to be the square root of the mean value of the square of the function over an integral number of complete periods. If we denote the root-mean-square value of $f(t)$ by S then

$$S^2 = \frac{1}{nT}\int_0^{nT} f^2(t) \; \mathrm{d}t = \frac{1}{T}\int_0^T f^2(t) \; \mathrm{d}t. \qquad (6)$$

Making use of Parseval's theorem (after a simple change of variable) we find that

$$S^2 = \bar{f}^2 + \tfrac{1}{2}\sum_{n=1}^{\infty}(a_n^2 + b_n^2). \qquad (7)$$

Now $a_n \cos (2n\pi t/T) + b_n \sin (2n\pi t/T)$ is the n-th harmonic of the function and its amplitude is c_n where $c_n^2 = a_n^2 + b_n^2$. Hence, from equation (7) we have:

Theorem 5.

The root-mean-square value S of a periodic function is given by

$$S^2 = \bar{f}^2 + \tfrac{1}{2}\sum_{n=1}^{\infty} c_n^2,$$

where f is the mean value and $c_1, c_2, \ldots$ are the amplitudes of the successive harmonics of the function.

4. DIFFERENTIATION OF FOURIER SERIES

Suppose that $f(x)$ is defined in the interval $(0, 2\pi)$ and has Fourier coefficients

$$a_n = \frac{1}{\pi}\int_0^{2\pi} f(x) \cos nx \; \mathrm{d}x, \; b_n = \frac{1}{\pi}\int_0^{2\pi} f(x) \sin nx \; \mathrm{d}x. \qquad (1)$$

Let us *assume* that the derivative $f'(x)$ possesses a Fourier series

$$f'(x) = \tfrac{1}{2}A_0 + \sum_{n=1}^{\infty}(A_n \cos nx + B_n \sin nx)$$

The Fourier coefficients can be calculated in the usual way.

$$A_0 = \frac{1}{\pi} \int_0^{2\pi} f'(x) \, dx = \frac{1}{\pi}[f(2\pi-0)-f(0+)],$$

$$A_n = \frac{1}{\pi} \int_0^{2\pi} f'(x) \cos nx \, dx = \frac{1}{\pi}[f(2\pi-0)-f(0+)]+nb_n,$$

$$B_n = \frac{1}{\pi} \int_0^{2\pi} f'(x) \sin nx \, dx = -na_n.$$

From these formulae it follows that

$$f'(x) = \sum_{n=1}^{\infty} (nb_n \cos nx - na_n \sin nx)$$

if and only if $f(2\pi-0)=f(0+)$, i.e. the Fourier series of $f'(x)$ is equal to the series obtained by term-by-term differentiation of the Fourier series of $f(x)$ if and only if the function $f'(x)$ has a Fourier series and if $f(x)$ satisfies the condition

$$f(2\pi-0)=f(0+).$$

This equation merely expresses the fact that the periodic extension of the function $f(x)$ is continuous at the points $x=0$, $x=2\pi$.

The above argument can be made precise to yield:

Theorem 6.

If $f(x)$ is continuous in $(0, 2\pi)$ and if $f(+0)=f(2\pi-0)$ and if its derivative $f'(x)$ is piecewise-smooth in that interval then the series

$$\sum_{n=1}^{\infty} (nb_n \cos nx - na_n \sin nx)$$

in which a_n, b_n are the Fourier coefficients of $f(x)$ converges to the sum

$$\tfrac{1}{2}[f'(x+0)+f'(x-0)]$$

at each point of the interval at which $f'(x)$ has a right-hand and a left-hand derivative.

The theorem also applies (with appropriate changes of variable) to the other types of Fourier series

To illustrate the necessity of the condition $f(2\pi)=f(0)$ we consider the Fourier series of the function $f(x)=x$, $0<x<2\pi$. For this function it is easy to show that the Fourier coefficients are

$$a_0=2\pi, \quad a_n=0, \quad b_n=-\frac{2}{n}$$

so that, for $0<x<2\pi$,

$$x=\pi-2\sum_{n=1}^{\infty}\frac{\sin nx}{n}.$$

But the trigonometrical series

$$-2\sum_{n=1}^{\infty}\cos nx$$

obtained by differentiating this series term-by-term does not converge to 1 (i.e. to the derivative of x) in the interval $(0, 2\pi)$. Indeed, since the n-th term does not tend to zero as $n\to\infty$, the series is divergent for all values of x.

5. TRIGONOMETRICAL POLYNOMIALS AND FOURIER POLYNOMIALS

Any finite sum of the kind

$$\Phi_n(x)=\tfrac{1}{2}\alpha_0+\sum_{r=1}^{n}(\alpha_r\cos rx+\beta_r\sin rx) \tag{1}$$

is called a *trigonometrical polynomial of degree n*, whatever the form of the coefficients α_r, β_r. If, however,

$$f_n(x)=\tfrac{1}{2}a_0+\sum_{r=1}^{n}(a_r\cos rx+b_r\sin rx) \tag{2}$$

where

$$a_r=\frac{1}{\pi}\int_0^{2\pi}f(x)\cos rx\,\mathrm{d}x, \quad b_r=\frac{1}{\pi}\int_0^{2\pi}f(x)\sin rx\,\mathrm{d}x, \tag{3}$$

$$(r=0, 1, 2, \ldots, n)$$

then we say that $f_n(x)$ is the *Fourier polynomial of degree n* of the function $f(x)$.

Suppose now that we are given a function $f(x)$ and that we wish to approximate to it, in the interval, $(0, 2\pi)$ by a trigonometrical polynomial $\Phi_n(x)$, of the type (1), giving the best mean square approximation, i.e. we wish to find a trigonometrical polynomial $\Phi_n(x)$ such that the integral

$$I_n = \int_0^{2\pi} [f(x) - \Phi_n(x)]^2 \, dx \qquad (4)$$

is a minimum. If we substitute from (1) into this expression and carry out the integrations we find that

$$I_n = \int_0^{2\pi} [f(x)]^2 \, dx + \tfrac{1}{2}\pi\alpha_0^2 + \pi \sum_{r=1}^n (\alpha_r^2 + \beta_r^2) - \pi a_0\alpha_0$$

$$- 2\pi \sum_{r=1}^n (a_r\alpha_r + b_r\beta_r) \qquad (5)$$

where $a_0, a_1, \ldots, a_n, b_1, \ldots, b_n$ are the first $2n+1$ Fourier coefficients of $f(x)$, defined by equations (3). Similarly if we use $f_n(x)$ instead of $\Phi_n(x)$, where $f_n(x)$ is the trigonometrical polynomial (1) with α_r, β_r replaced by a_r, b_r we have

$$J_n = \int_0^{2\pi} [f(x) - f_n(x)]^2 \, dx = \int_0^{2\pi} [f(x)]^2 \, dx - \tfrac{1}{2}\pi a_0^2$$

$$- \pi \sum_{r=1}^n (a_r + b_r^2) \qquad (6)$$

so that

$$I_n - J_n = \tfrac{1}{2}\pi(\alpha_0 - a_0)^2 + \pi \sum_{r=1}^n [(\alpha_r - a_r)^2 + (\beta_r - b_r)^2].$$

Since each term on the right of this relation is positive except when $\alpha_r = a_r$, $\beta_r = b_r$, $(r = 0, 1, \ldots, n)$, we have proved:

Theorem 7.

Among all trigonometrical polynomials of degree n, that which gives the best mean square approximation to a given function $f(x)$ is the Fourier polynomial $f_n(x)$ of that function.

In the integral defining J_n the integrand is always positive or zero, so that $J_n \geqslant 0$. Using this in equation (6) we obtain Bessel's inequality

$$\frac{1}{\pi}\int_0^{2\pi}[f(x)]^2 \, \mathrm{d}x \geqslant \tfrac{1}{2}a_0^2 + \sum_{r=1}^n (a_r^2 + b_r^2) \qquad (7)$$

for all positive integers n.

Theorem 7 is easily generalized to the orthonormal sets of functions $\phi_1(x)$, $\phi_2(x)$, ... introduced in section 8 of Chapter I. If we form a function

$$\Phi_n(x) = \sum_{m=1}^n c_m \phi_m(x)$$

then

$$I_n = \int_a^b [f(x) - \Phi_n(x)]^2 \, \mathrm{d}x$$

$$= \int_a^b [f(x)]^2 \, \mathrm{d}x - 2\sum_{m=1}^n c_m(f, \phi_m) + \sum_{m=1}^n c_m^2$$

which is a minimum if

$$c_m = (f, \phi_m)$$

where, as in equation (3),

$$(f, \phi_m) = \int_a^b f(x)\phi_m(x) \, \mathrm{d}x.$$

Hence the best mean square approximation to $f(x)$ is given by the polynomial

$$f_n(x) = \sum_{m=1}^n (f, \phi_m)\phi_m(x)$$

made up of the first n terms of the infinite series

$$\sum_{m=1}^{\infty} (f, \phi_m) \phi_m(x)$$

representing $f(x)$. This may be stated as:

Theorem 8.

If $\phi_i(x)$, $i = 1, 2, \ldots$ form an orthonormal set of functions defined over (a, b) then among all polynomials

$$\Phi_n(x) = \sum_{n=1}^{n} c_m \phi_m(x)$$

of given degree n, that which gives the best mean square approximation to a function $f(x)$ defined in (a, b) is the Fourier polynomial

$$f_n(x) = \sum_{m=1}^{n} (f, \phi_m) \phi_m(x).$$

6. GIBBS'S PHENOMENON

We have seen in the last section that a properly chosen trigonometrical series can give a least-squares fit, even for a function which has a finite number of finite discontinuities. We shall now show that this fit exhibits a certain peculiarity near a discontinuity, which leads to certain difficulties when such series are used to compute the value of a function near one of its discontinuities.

It is obvious that the sum $S_n(x)$ of the first n terms of a Fourier series cannot fit a finite discontinuity, since it cannot possibly have the infinite slope demanded by the discontinuity. It is found that, in trying to achieve this infinite slope, the finite series $S_n(x)$ actually overshoots the discontinuity by an appreciable amount. These additional 'peaks' being of vanishingly small width do not affect the least-squares fit, which depends on integration, but their presence indicates the limitations of the whole process of representing a function by a Fourier series.

We shall make these remarks more specific by considering a simple example. The Fourier series periodic in x with period 2π representing the function

$$f(x) = \frac{\pi - x}{\pi}, \quad 0 < x < 2\pi$$

is

$$S(x) = \frac{2}{\pi} \sum_{r=1}^{\infty} \frac{\sin rx}{r}.$$

If we denote by $S_n(x)$ the sum of the first n terms of this series then, differentiating with respect to x, we find that

$$S'_n(x) = \frac{2}{\pi} \sum_{r=1}^{n} \cos rx = \frac{2}{\pi} \cdot \frac{\cos (\frac{1}{2}n + \frac{1}{2})x \cdot \sin \frac{1}{2}nx}{\sin \frac{1}{2}x}. \quad (1)$$

Integrating this expression we obtain the formula

$$S_n(x) = \frac{2}{\pi} \int_0^x \frac{\cos (\frac{1}{2}n + \frac{1}{2})u \cdot \sin \frac{1}{2}nu}{\sin \frac{1}{2}u} \, du \quad (2)$$

for the finite sum $S_n(x)$.

Now from equation (1) we find that the turning values of the function $S_n(x)$ are given by $x = (2r+1)\pi/(n+1)$, $x = (r+1)\pi/(n+1)$, $(r = 0, 1, 2, \ldots)$ the former set giving maxima and the latter minima. Then $\xi_n = \pi/(n+1)$ yields the maximum of $S_n(x)$ in the neighbourhood of $x = 0$.

Consider now the difference

$$S_n(\xi_n) - f(\xi_n) = \frac{2}{\pi} \int_0^{\xi_n} \frac{\cos (\frac{1}{2}n + \frac{1}{2})u \cdot \sin \frac{1}{2}nu}{\sin \frac{1}{2}u} \, du - 1 + \frac{\xi_n}{\pi}.$$

Now

$$\frac{\cos (\frac{1}{2}n + \frac{1}{2})u \cdot \sin \frac{1}{2}nu}{\sin \frac{1}{2}u}$$
$$= \frac{\sin (n + \frac{1}{2})u}{u} + \left(\frac{1}{2 \sin \frac{1}{2}u} - \frac{1}{u} \right) \sin (n + \frac{1}{2})u - \frac{1}{2}$$

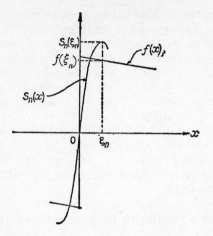

FIG. 9

so that

$$S_n(\xi_n) - f(\xi_n) = I(\xi_n) + J(\xi_n) - 1$$

where

$$I(\xi_n) = \frac{2}{\pi}\int_0^{\xi_n} \frac{\sin(n+\frac{1}{2})u}{u}\,du = \frac{2}{\pi}\int_0^{(n+\frac{1}{2})\xi_n} \frac{\sin v}{v}dv$$

$$J(\xi_n) = \frac{2}{\pi}\int_0^{\xi_n}\left(\frac{1}{2\sin\frac{1}{2}u} - \frac{1}{u}\right)\sin(n+\frac{1}{2})u\,du.$$

Now, since

$$\frac{1}{2\sin\frac{1}{2}u} - \frac{1}{u}$$

is continuous at $u=0$, it follows from Lemma **1** that $J(\xi_n)\to 0$ as $n\to\infty$. Also

$$I(\xi_n)\to\frac{2}{\pi}\int_0^\pi \frac{\sin v}{v}\,dv$$

and the numerical value of this integral is 1·179. Hence as $n\to\infty$ $S_n(\xi_n) - f(\xi_n)\to 0\cdot179$ it being remembered that $\xi_n\to 0$ as $n\to\infty$.

In this way we see that the series in trying to follow the discontinuity overshoots the mark by about 18 per cent over a range of vanishingly small length before settling down to the correct value of the function. Since the range over which the overshooting at a discontinuity occurs is of vanishingly small width we should expect an integral of the series to give correct values but should be cautious in differentiating the series.

This phenomenon (which occurs for the finite sum of the Fourier series of any discontinuous function) is usually called the 'Gibbs Phenomenon' although the essential idea seems to have been conceived earlier by Wilbraham and by du Bois-Raymond.

7. HURWITZ'S SOLUTION OF THE ISOPERIMETRIC PROBLEM

The 'isoperimetric problem' of the ancient Greeks is that of finding the shape of a simple closed curve of length l enclosing the maximum area. That the circle encloses the maximum area was conjectured early and 'proved' by various methods but rigorous proofs were obtained only as a result of the development of modern techniques. We shall outline an ingenious proof, making use of Fourier series, which was given by A. Hurwitz in 1902.

Analytically the problem may be formulated as that of finding an arc with parametric equations

$$x = x(s), \quad y = y(s), \quad 0 \leqslant s \leqslant l \qquad (1)$$

in which $x(s)$ and $y(s)$ are continuous functions of the arc length s with piecewise-smooth derivatives $x'(s)$, $y'(s)$ with respect to s, yielding a maximum value of the area integral

$$A = \tfrac{1}{2} \int_0^l (xy' - x'y) \, ds \qquad (2)$$

and satisfying the conditions

$$x(0) = x(l), \quad y(0) = y(l).$$

With these assumptions we may write

$$x = \tfrac{1}{2}a_0 + \sum_{n=1}^{\infty}\left(a_n \cos \frac{2n\pi s}{l} + b_n \sin \frac{2n\pi s}{l}\right)$$
$$y = \tfrac{1}{2}\alpha_0 + \sum_{n=1}^{\infty}\left(\alpha_n \cos \frac{2n\pi s}{l} + \beta_n \sin \frac{2n\pi s}{l}\right) \Biggr\} \quad (3)$$

and differentiate term by term to obtain

$$x' = \frac{2\pi}{l}\sum_{n=1}^{\infty}\left(nb_n \cos \frac{2n\pi s}{l} - na_n \sin \frac{2n\pi s}{l}\right)$$
$$y' = \frac{2\pi}{l}\sum_{n=1}^{\infty}\left(n\beta_n \cos \frac{2n\pi s}{l} - n\alpha_n \sin \frac{2n\pi s}{l}\right) \Biggr\} \quad (4)$$

Since s denotes arc length we have the fundamental identity

$$x'^2 + y'^2 = 1$$

which may be written in the form

$$l^2 = l\int_0^l (x'^2 + y'^2)\, ds. \quad (5)$$

Substituting from (4) into (5) and performing the integrations we find that

$$\frac{l^2}{4\pi} = \tfrac{1}{2}\pi \sum_{n=1}^{\infty} n^2(a_n^2 + b_n^2 + \alpha_n^2 + \beta_n^2). \quad (6)$$

Similarly from equation (2) we find that

$$A = \pi \sum_{n=1}^{\infty} n(a_n\beta_n - b_n\alpha_n). \quad (7)$$

From equations (6) and (7) we obtain the relation

$$A - \frac{l^2}{4\pi} = -\tfrac{1}{2}\pi \sum_{n=1}^{\infty} \{n^2(a_n^2 + b_n^2 + \alpha_n^2 + \beta_n^2) - 2n(a_n\beta_n - \alpha_n b_n)\}$$

$$= -\tfrac{1}{2}\pi \sum_{n=1}^{\infty} \{(na_n - \beta_n)^2 + (nb_n + \alpha_n)^2 + (n^2-1)(\alpha_n^2 + \beta_n^2)\}$$

$$\leqslant 0.$$

43

For the equality sign to hold we would need to have
$$\alpha_1 = -b_1, \quad \beta_1 = a_1$$
and all the other coefficients zero, in which case the curve has parametric equations
$$x = \tfrac{1}{2}a_0 + a_1 \cos t + b_1 \sin t$$
$$y = \tfrac{1}{2}\alpha_0 - b_1 \cos t + a_1 \sin t$$
and is therefore the circle
$$(x - \tfrac{1}{2}a_0)^2 + (y - \tfrac{1}{2}\alpha_0)^2 = a_1^2 + b_1^2.$$
It follows therefore that all continuous smooth closed curves with piecewise-smooth derivatives satisfy the isoperimetric inequality

$$A - \frac{l^2}{4\pi} \leqslant 0$$

where the perimeter is l and the area is A. We have shown also that the equality sign holds if and only if the boundary curve is a circle, so proving the isoperimetric character of the circle.

EXERCISES ON CHAPTER III

1. The Fourier series of a function $f(x)$ in the range $(0, 2\pi)$ is
$$\tfrac{1}{2}a_0 + \sum_{n=1}^{\infty} \{a_n \cos nx + b_n \sin nx\}.$$

Prove that the Fourier series of the function $\int_0^x f(y)\mathrm{d}y$ in the same range is
$$\tfrac{1}{2}A_0 + \sum_{n=1}^{\infty} \{A_n \cos nx + B_n \sin nx\}.$$
where
$$A_0 = 2\pi a_0 - \frac{1}{\pi}\int_0^{2\pi} xf(x)\mathrm{d}x, \quad A_n = -\frac{1}{n}b_n, \quad B_n = -\frac{1}{n}a_0 + \frac{1}{n}a_n.$$

Verify that these relations are satisfied when $f(x)$ is the function
$$f(x) = \begin{cases} 0 & (0 \leqslant x \leqslant \pi); \\ 1 & (\pi < x < 2\pi). \end{cases}$$

2. If
$$f(x) \sim \tfrac{1}{2}a_0 + \sum_{n=1}^{\infty} \{a_n \cos nx + b_n \sin nx\}$$

44

for $0 \leqslant x \leqslant 2\pi$, show that

$$\sum_{n=1}^{\infty} \frac{b_n}{n} = \frac{1}{2\pi} \int_0^{2\pi} (\pi - x) f(x) dx.$$

Find the Fourier coefficients of $f(x) = \pi - x$, $0 \leqslant x < 2\pi$ and deduce that

$$\sum_{n=1}^{\infty} \frac{1}{n^2} = \frac{\pi^2}{6}.$$

3. A function $f(x)$ is defined in the interval $-\pi \leqslant x < \pi$ by the formulae

$$f(x) = \begin{cases} \frac{1}{2}\pi - x, & 0 \leqslant x < \pi, \\ \frac{1}{2}\pi + x, & -\pi \leqslant x \leqslant 0. \end{cases}$$

Obtain the Fourier coefficients of the function and sketch the graph of the Fourier series of the function in the interval $(-2\pi, 2\pi)$.
Deduce that

$$\sum_{r=1}^{\infty} \frac{(-1)^{r-1}}{(2r-1)^3} = \frac{\pi^3}{32}.$$

4. If

$$f(x) = \begin{cases} \pi + x, & -\pi < x < 0; \\ \frac{1}{2}\pi, & x = -\pi, 0, \\ x, & 0 < x < \pi; \end{cases}$$

show that, for $-\pi \leqslant x \leqslant \pi$.

$$f(x) = \frac{1}{2}\pi - \sum_{n=1}^{\infty} \frac{\sin 2nx}{n}.$$

Deduce that, if $0 \leqslant x \leqslant \pi$,

$$\sum_{n=1}^{\infty} \frac{\cos 2nx}{n^2} = x^2 - \pi x + S$$

where

$$S = \sum_{n=1}^{\infty} \frac{1}{n^2}.$$

By putting $x = \frac{1}{2}\pi$ or otherwise, prove that $S = \pi^2/6$, and deduce that

(i) $\displaystyle\sum_{n=1}^{\infty} \frac{\sin 2nx}{n^3} = \frac{1}{3}x(\pi - x)(\pi - 2x)$, $0 \leqslant x \leqslant \pi$;

(ii) $\displaystyle\frac{1}{1^3} - \frac{1}{3^3} + \frac{1}{5^3} - \ldots = \frac{\pi^3}{32}.$

5. Prove that, if n is zero or a positive integer,

(i) $\displaystyle\int_{-\pi}^{\pi} e^{ax} \cos nx\, dx = (-1)^n \frac{2a \sinh (\pi a)}{a^2 + n^2}$,

(ii) $\displaystyle\int_{-\pi}^{\pi} e^{ax} \sin nx\, dx = (-1)^{n-1} \frac{2n \sinh (\pi a)}{a^2 + n^2}.$

Hence show that, if $-\pi < x < \pi$,

$$e^{ax} = \frac{1}{\pi}\sinh(\pi a)\left\{\frac{1}{a} + 2\sum_{n=1}^{\infty}(-1)^n\frac{a\cos nx}{a^2+n^2} - 2\sum_{n=1}^{\infty}(-1)^n\frac{n\sin nx}{a^2+n^2}\right\}.$$

State the value of the expression on the right when x has the value π, and deduce that

$$\pi\coth a\pi = \frac{1}{a} + \sum_{n=1}^{\infty}\frac{2a}{a^2+n^2}.$$

Prove that, if $-\pi \leqslant x \leqslant \pi$,

$$\sinh ax = \frac{\sinh(\pi a)}{\pi}\left\{x + 2\sum_{n=1}^{\infty}(-1)^n\frac{a^2\sin nx}{n(a^2+n^2)}\right\}.$$

Deduce, or otherwise show, that

$$\frac{\pi}{\sinh \pi a} = \frac{1}{a} + 2\sum_{n=1}^{\infty}(-1)^n\frac{a}{a^2+n^2}.$$

6. Show that, if $-\pi < x < \pi$,

$$x^2 = \tfrac{1}{3}\pi^2 + 4\sum_{n=1}^{\infty}(-1)^n\frac{\cos nx}{n^2},$$

and deduce the corresponding Fourier series of
(i) x; (ii) x^3,
in the same interval.

7. Show that, for $-\pi \leqslant x \leqslant \pi$,

$$x\sin x = 1 - \tfrac{1}{2}\cos x - 2\left(\frac{\cos 2x}{1.3} - \frac{\cos 3x}{2.4} + \dots\right).$$

Deduce that

(i) $x\cos x = -\tfrac{1}{2}\sin x + 2\left(\dfrac{2\sin 2x}{1.3} - \dfrac{3\sin 3x}{2.4} + \dots\right)$,
for $-\pi < x < \pi$;

(ii) $x\cos^2\tfrac{1}{2}x = \tfrac{3}{4}\sin x + \dfrac{\sin 2x}{1.2.3} - \dfrac{\sin 3x}{2.3.4} + \dots$,
for $-\pi \leqslant x \leqslant \pi$.

What are the values of the series on the right-hand sides of (i) and (ii) in the range from $x=\pi$ to $x=3\pi$?

8. A function $f(t)$ has period π, its value is $\sin 2t$ for $0 \leqslant t < \tfrac{1}{2}\pi$ and is zero for $\tfrac{1}{2}\pi \leqslant t < \pi$. Show that

$$f(t) = \frac{1}{\pi} + \tfrac{1}{2}\sin 2t - \frac{2}{\pi}\sum_{n=1}^{\infty}\frac{\cos 4nt}{(2n-1)(2n+1)}.$$

Deduce that

$$\sum_{n=1}^{\infty}\frac{1}{(2n-1)^2(2n+1)^2} = \frac{\pi^2-8}{16}.$$

From the expansion of $f(t)$ deduce the value of the series

$$\frac{\sin 4t}{1.2.3} + \frac{\sin 8t}{3.4.5} + \frac{\sin 12t}{5.6.7} + \dots$$

in the range $0 \leqslant t \leqslant \pi$.

46

EXERCISES ON CHAPTER III

9. Find the Fourier series of the function $f(x)$ defined by the equations

$$f(x) = \begin{cases} 0, & -\pi < x < 0; \\ 1, & 0 < x < \pi, \end{cases}$$

and, using Parseval's theorem, deduce that

$$\sum_{n=1}^{\infty} \frac{1}{(2n-1)^2} = \frac{\pi^2}{8}.$$

CHAPTER FOUR

Applications in the Solution of Partial Differential Equations

---

1. THE TRANSVERSE VIBRATIONS OF A STRETCHED STRING

If a uniform string is stretched to a tension T between two fixed points O and A distant l apart then if we take O to be the origin of co-ordinates and OA to be the x-axis, the transverse displacement $y(x, t)$ at time t satisfies the partial differential equation

$$c^2 \frac{\partial^2 y}{\partial x^2} = \frac{\partial^2 y}{\partial t^2} \tag{1}$$

where $c^2 = T/\rho$, ρl being the mass of the string. Since the string is fixed at the points O and A then we have the boundary conditions

$$y(0, t) = y(l, t) = 0, \text{ for all } t. \tag{2}$$

We might suppose that the transverse motion of the string is caused by the string being pulled aside to a prescribed shape and then released from rest, i.e. we may assume that at $t = 0$,

$$y(x, 0) = f(x), \ 0 \leqslant x \leqslant l \tag{3}$$

$$\frac{\partial y}{\partial t} = 0, \ 0 \leqslant x \leqslant l, \ t = 0. \tag{4}$$

To solve the equation (1) we assume that
$$y(x, t) = X(x) T(t)$$
where $X(x)$ is a function of x only, and $T(t)$ is a function of t only. Substituting this form in equation (1) we find that

48

$$\frac{X''}{X} = \frac{T''}{c^2 T},$$

from which it follows that

$$X'' + \alpha^2 X = 0, \quad T'' + c^2 \alpha^2 T = 0,$$

where α^2 is a constant. If (2) is to be satisfied we must take $\alpha = n\pi/l$,

$$X = \sin (n\pi x/l)$$

with n an integer. Assuming this value of α and ensuring that the boundary condition (4) is satisfied we obtain

$$T = \cos (n\pi ct/l).$$

It follows that

$$\sin \left(\frac{n\pi x}{l}\right) \cos \left(\frac{n\pi ct}{l}\right)$$

is a solution of equation (1) for any positive integer n and hence that, if the b_n are constant, so also is

$$y(x, t) = \sum_{n=1}^{\infty} b_n \sin \frac{n\pi x}{l} \cos \frac{n\pi ct}{l}. \tag{5}$$

This solution of equation (1) satisfies the initial condition (4) and the end conditions (2). It will only satisfy the other initial condition (3) if we can find the b_n such that

$$f(x) = \sum_{n=1}^{\infty} b_n \sin \frac{n\pi x}{l}. \tag{6}$$

This is the problem which we discussed in section 4 of Chapter I. We find that

$$b_n = \frac{2}{l} \int_0^l f(u) \sin \frac{n\pi u}{l} \, du. \tag{7}$$

Substituting from equation (7) into equation (5) we obtain the solution

$$y(x, t) = \frac{2}{l} \sum_{n=1}^{\infty} \left\{ \int_0^l f(u) \sin \frac{n\pi u}{l} \, du \right\} \sin \frac{n\pi x}{l} \cos \frac{n\pi ct}{l}. \tag{8}$$

49

Example 1. *Find the solution of the wave equation* (1) *which satisfies the conditions:*

(i) $y=0$ *at* $x=0$, $x=l$ *for all values of* t;

(ii) $\partial y/\partial t=0$ *at* $t=0$ *for all values of* x;

(iii) $y=2\epsilon x/l$, $0<x<\frac{1}{2}l$, $y=2\epsilon(1-x/l)$, $\frac{1}{2}l<x<l$ *when* $t=0$.

This is the problem considered above with

$$f(u)=\begin{cases}2\epsilon u/l, & 0\leqslant u\leqslant\frac{1}{2}l;\\2\epsilon(l-u)/l, & \frac{1}{2}l\leqslant u\leqslant l.\end{cases}$$

so that

$$b_n=\frac{4\epsilon}{l^2}\int_0^{\frac{1}{2}l}u\sin\frac{n\pi u}{l}\,\mathrm{d}u+\frac{4\epsilon}{l^2}\int_{\frac{1}{2}l}^l(l-u)\sin\frac{n\pi u}{l}\,\mathrm{d}u,$$

from which it follows by an integration by parts that

$$b_n=\frac{8\epsilon}{\pi^2 n^2}\sin\left(\tfrac{1}{2}n\pi\right),$$

showing that $b_{2r}=0$ and

$$b_{2r-1}=\frac{8\epsilon}{\pi^2}\cdot\frac{(-1)^{r-1}}{(2r-1)^2},$$

and hence that the required solution is

$$y(x,t)=\frac{8\epsilon}{\pi^2}\sum_{r=1}^{\infty}\frac{(-1)^{r-1}}{(2r-1)^2}\sin\frac{(2r-1)\pi x}{l}\cos\frac{(2r-1)\pi ct}{l}. \quad (9)$$

If instead of the initial conditions (3) and (4) we have the conditions

$$y(x,0)=0, \quad \frac{\partial y}{\partial t}=g(x), \quad 0\leqslant x\leqslant l \quad (10)$$

then, instead of the solution (5) we have

$$y(x,t)=\sum_{n=1}^{\infty}B_n\sin\frac{n\pi x}{l}\sin\frac{n\pi ct}{l} \quad (11)$$

for which

$$\frac{\partial y}{\partial t} = \frac{\pi c}{l} \sum_{n=1}^{\infty} n B_n \sin \frac{n \pi x}{l} \cos \frac{n \pi c t}{l}.$$

Putting $t=0$ in this expression we find that the B_n must be chosen in such a way that

$$g(x) = \frac{\pi c}{l} \sum_{n=1}^{\infty} n B_n \sin \frac{n \pi x}{l}$$

so that

$$B_n = \frac{2}{\pi c n} \int_0^l g(u) \sin \frac{n \pi u}{l} \, \mathrm{d}u.$$

We shall give an example of the use of this formula in the next section.

2. IMPULSIVE FUNCTIONS

If an impulse P is applied to a small length ϵ of the string centred at the point $x=a$, then, if we denote the initial velocity of this portion by v then $\rho \epsilon v = P$ so that, in this instance the initial velocity of the string is given by the equation

$$g(x) = \frac{P}{\rho} \delta_\epsilon(x, a) \tag{1}$$

where $\delta_\epsilon(x, a)$ denotes the function defined by the equations

$$\delta_\epsilon(x, a) = \begin{cases} 0, & 0 \leqslant x < a - \tfrac{1}{2}\epsilon, \\ \dfrac{1}{\epsilon}, & a - \tfrac{1}{2}\epsilon \leqslant x \leqslant a + \tfrac{1}{2}\epsilon, \\ 0, & a + \tfrac{1}{2}\epsilon < x \leqslant l, \end{cases}$$

(cf. Fig. 10). To find the coefficients in the Fourier expansion

$$\delta_\epsilon(x, a) = \sum_{n=1}^{\infty} b_n \sin \frac{n \pi x}{l}$$

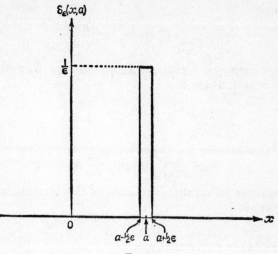

FIG. 10

we have the equation

$$b_n = \frac{2}{l\epsilon} \int_{a-\frac{1}{2}\epsilon}^{a+\frac{1}{2}\epsilon} \sin \frac{n\pi x}{l} \, dx$$

from which it follows that

$$b_n = \frac{2}{l} \left[\frac{\sin \dfrac{n\pi\epsilon}{2l}}{\dfrac{n\pi\epsilon}{2l}} \right] \sin \frac{n\pi a}{l}. \tag{2}$$

As $\epsilon \to 0$,

$$b_n \to \frac{2}{l} \sin \frac{n\pi a}{l}$$

so that if we write *symbolically*

$$\delta(x, a) = \lim_{\epsilon=0} \delta_\epsilon(x, a) \tag{3}$$

we find that

$$\delta(x, a) = \frac{2}{l}\sum_{n=1}^{\infty}\sin\frac{n\pi x}{l}\sin\frac{n\pi a}{l}. \tag{4}$$

We say 'symbolically' here because $\delta(x, a)$ as defined by equation (3) is not in fact a function in the ordinary sense. It is indeed a 'generalized' function, the treatment of which is beyond the scope of this book. The Fourier expansion (4) is however very useful in the discussion of problems in which a disturbance is concentrated at the point $x = a$ and is such that

$$\int_0^l \delta(x, a)\,\mathrm{d}x = 1.$$

As an example of its use we have:

Example 2. *An impulse P is applied at the point $x = a$ perpendicular to a string stretched to a tension T between the points $x = 0$ and $x = l$. Find the displacement of the string at any subsequent time.*

In the notation of the last section

$$g(x) = \frac{P}{\rho}\delta(x, a)$$

so that the required solution is

$$y = \sum_{n=1}^{\infty}B_n\sin\frac{n\pi x}{l}\sin\frac{n\pi ct}{l}$$

where

$$\frac{P}{\rho}\delta(x, a) = \frac{\pi c}{l}\sum_{n=1}^{\infty}nB_n\sin\frac{n\pi x}{l}. \tag{5}$$

Comparing equations (4) and (5) we find that

$$nB_n = \frac{2P}{\pi\rho c}\sin\frac{n\pi a}{l}$$

yielding the solution

$$y = \frac{2P}{\pi\rho c}\sum_{n=1}^{\infty}\frac{1}{n}\sin\frac{n\pi a}{l}\sin\frac{n\pi x}{l}\sin\frac{n\pi ct}{l}.$$

Another example of the use of $\delta(x, a)$ is provided by Problem **10** at the end of the Chapter.

3. LAPLACE'S EQUATION

We shall make use of the theory of Fourier series to derive solutions of the two-dimensional Laplace's equation

$$\frac{\partial^2 \psi}{\partial x^2} + \frac{\partial^2 \psi}{\partial y^2} = 0 \qquad (1)$$

for rectangles and infinite strips. If we assume the existence of solutions of the type

$$\psi(x, y) = X(x) Y(y), \qquad (2)$$

then we find that the functions X and Y must be such that

$$-X''/X = +Y''/Y,$$

and it follows that the functions on each side of this equation must be equal to a constant, ξ^2 say, so that

$$X'' + \xi^2 X = 0, \quad Y'' - \xi^2 Y = 0.$$

These equations have general solutions

$$X = A \sin \xi x + B \cos \xi x, \quad Y = Ce^{-\xi y} + De^{\xi y}. \qquad (3)$$

If we assume that $\xi > 0$ and wish solutions which tend to zero as $y \to \infty$ we must take $D = 0$, and if we wish solutions satisfying the condition

$$\psi(0, y) = 0, \qquad (4)$$

we must take $B = 0$. Hence the function

$$e^{-\xi y} \sin \xi x$$

tends to zero as $y \to \infty$ and satisfies the condition (4). If we impose the further condition

$$\psi(l, y) = 0 \qquad (5)$$

we must choose the constant ξ in such a way that $\sin \xi l = 0$, i.e. we must choose ξ to be one of the values $n\pi/l$, $(n = 1, 2, 3, \ldots)$.

Adding the solutions obtained in this way we derive the solution

$$\psi(x, y) = \sum_{n=1}^{\infty} b_n \sin\left(\frac{n\pi x}{l}\right) e^{-n\pi y/l}. \qquad (6)$$

For instance if ψ satisfies the equations (1), (4), (5) and the conditions $\psi \to 0$ as $y \to \infty$, $\psi(x, 0) = f(x)$, it is given by the equation (6) with the coefficients b_n such that

$$f(x) = \sum_{n=1}^{\infty} b_n \sin\left(\frac{n\pi x}{l}\right)$$

so that

$$b_n = \frac{2}{l} \int_0^l f(u) \sin\frac{n\pi u}{l} \, du. \qquad (7)$$

To illustrate this method we have:

Example 3. *Find the solution $\psi(x, y)$ of Laplace's equation satisfying the conditions*

    (i) $\psi \to 0$ *as* $y \to \infty$;
    (ii) $\psi = 0$ *for* $x = 0$ *and for* $x = l$;
    (iii) $\psi(x, 0) = \begin{cases} x, \text{ for } 0 \leqslant x \leqslant \frac{1}{2}l \\ l - x \text{ for } \frac{1}{2}l \leqslant x \leqslant l. \end{cases}$

The solution is given by equation (6) with b_n given by (7), that is, by

$$b_n = \frac{2}{l} \int_0^{\frac{1}{2}l} u \sin\frac{n\pi u}{l} \, du + \frac{2}{l} \int_{\frac{1}{2}l}^l (l-u) \sin\frac{n\pi u}{l} \, du,$$

from which it follows that

$$b_n = \frac{4l}{\pi^2} \frac{\sin\left(\frac{1}{2}n\pi\right)}{n^2}.$$

The required solution is therefore

$$\psi(x, y) = \frac{4l}{\pi^2} \sum_{r=1}^{\infty} \frac{(-1)^{r-1}}{(2r-1)^2} \sin\frac{(2r-1)\pi x}{l} e^{-(2r-1)\pi y/l}.$$

If, instead of the conditions (4) and (5), we have the conditions

$$\frac{\partial \psi}{\partial x} = 0, \ x = 0 \text{ and } x = l$$

we have the solution

$$\psi(x, y) = \frac{1}{2}a_0 + \sum_{n=1}^{\infty} a_n \cos\left(\frac{n\pi x}{l}\right) e^{-n\pi y/l}. \tag{8}$$

and if $\psi(x, 0) = g(x)$ then the coefficients a_n are such that

$$g(x) = \frac{1}{2}a_0 + \sum_{n=1}^{\infty} a_n \cos\left(\frac{n\pi x}{l}\right)$$

so that

$$a_n = \frac{2}{l} \int_0^l g(u) \cos\frac{n\pi u}{l} \, du. \tag{9}$$

As an example we have:

Example 4. *Find the solution $\psi(x, y)$ of Laplace's equation satisfying the conditions*
  (i) *ψ remains finite as $y \to \infty$;*
  (ii) *$\partial\psi/\partial x = 0$ when $x = 0$ and $x = l$;*
  (iii) *$\psi = l - x$ when $y = 0$ and $0 \leqslant x \leqslant l$.*
The solution is given by equation (8) with

$$a_0 = \frac{2}{l} \int_0^l (l-u) \, du = l,$$

$$a_n = \frac{2}{l} \int_0^l (l-u) \cos\frac{n\pi u}{l} \, du = \frac{2l}{\pi^2 n^2}[1 - (-1)^n]$$

that is

$$\psi(x, y) = \tfrac{1}{2}l + \frac{4l}{\pi^2} \sum_{r=1}^{\infty} \frac{1}{(2r-1)^2} \cos\frac{(2r-1)\pi x}{l} \cdot e^{-2(r-1)\pi y/l}.$$

If we wish to find a solution in a rectangular region $0 \leqslant x \leqslant l_1$, $0 \leqslant y \leqslant l_2$, we must take the full form for $Y(y)$ in (3). Suppose, for instance, that ψ is zero on the lines $x = 0$, $x = l_1$, $y = 0$. We must then take a solution of the form

$$\psi(x, y) = \sum_{n=1}^{\infty} b_n \sin\frac{n\pi x}{l_1} \sinh\frac{n\pi y}{l_1}. \tag{10}$$

If, in addition, $\psi = f(x)$ on the line $y = l_2$ then

$$f(x) = \sum_{n=1}^{\infty} b_n \sin \frac{n\pi x}{l_1} \sinh \frac{n\pi l_2}{l_1}, \ 0 \leqslant x \leqslant l_1,$$

from which it follows that

$$b_n \sinh \frac{n\pi l_2}{l_1} = \frac{2}{l_1} \int_0^{l_1} f(u) \sin \frac{n\pi u}{l_1} \, du. \tag{11}$$

To illustrate the method we have:

Example 5. *Find a solution $\psi(x, y)$ of Laplace's equation valid inside the rectangle $0 \leqslant x \leqslant l_1$, $0 \leqslant y \leqslant l_2$, and vanishing everywhere on the boundary except on the side $y = l_2$ where it has the value ψ_0.*

The solution is given by equation (10) with

$$b_n \sinh \frac{n\pi l_2}{l_1} = \frac{2\psi_0}{l_1} \int_0^{l_1} \sin \frac{n\pi u}{l_1} \, du = \frac{2\psi_0}{\pi n}(1 - \cos n\pi),$$

i.e. $b_{2r} = 0$, and

$$b_{2r-1} = \frac{4\psi_0}{\pi(2r-1)} \operatorname{cosech} \frac{(2r-1)\pi l_2}{l_1}$$

and the required solution is

$$\psi(x, y)$$
$$= \frac{4\psi_0}{\pi} \sum_{r=1}^{\infty} \frac{1}{(2r-1)} \operatorname{cosech} \frac{(2r-1)\pi l_2}{l_1} \sinh \frac{(2r-1)\pi y}{l_1} \sin \frac{(2r-1)\pi x}{l_1}.$$

4. THE LINEAR DIFFUSION EQUATION

The linear diffusion of heat is governed by the partial differential equation

$$\frac{\partial \theta}{\partial t} = k \frac{\partial^2 \theta}{\partial x^2}, \tag{1}$$

where x and t denote distance and time variables respectively, $\theta(x, t)$ denotes the temperature and k is a positive constant. This equation determines the flow of heat in a bar on the assumption that conditions are uniform across any section of the bar. In the solution of physical problems it is important to note that $\partial\theta/\partial x$ is the flux of heat across the section situated at a distance x from the origin of co-ordinates, so that if, for instance, the end section $x=l$ of a bar is insulated $(\partial\theta/\partial x)_l=0$.

If we write the solution of equation (1) in the form
$$\theta(x, t)=X(x)T(t)$$
then proceeding as in section 1 above we find that
$$X''+\alpha^2X=0, \ T'+k\alpha^2T=0. \tag{2}$$
Integrating the second of these equations we obtain the solution
$$T=\mathrm{e}^{-k\alpha^2t}.$$
It follows that, if we are interested in solutions of (1) which remain finite as $t\to\infty$ we must assume that α is real (or zero). Hence we can build up solutions of the form
$$\theta(x, t)=\sum_\alpha A_\alpha \cos(\alpha x+\epsilon_\alpha) \, \mathrm{e}^{-k\alpha^2t}. \tag{3}$$

The precise form of the solution will depend on the nature of the boundary conditions.

To illustrate the procedure we have:

Example 6. *Find a solution $\theta(x, t)$ of equation* (1) *satisfying the condition that θ remains finite as $t\to\infty$ and the further conditions:*

(i) $\partial\theta/\partial x=0$ *when $x=0$ and $x=c$ for all values of t;*
(ii) $\theta=\theta_0(1-x^2/c^2)$, $0<x<c$ *when $t=0$.*

If we write the basic solution in the form
$$(A \cos \alpha x+B \sin \alpha x) \, \mathrm{e}^{-k\alpha^2t}$$
we find that condition (i) is satisfied only if $B=0$ and $\sin(\alpha c)=0$, i.e. $\alpha=n\pi/c$, $(n=0, 1, 2, \ldots)$. Hence we obtain the solution
$$\theta(x, t)=\sum_{n=0}^{\infty} a_n \cos \frac{n\pi x}{c} \mathrm{e}^{-n^2\pi^2kt/c^2}$$

where, to satisfy (ii) we must choose the a_n to be such that

$$\theta_0(1-x^2/c^2)=\sum_{n=0}^{\infty} a_n \cos \frac{n\pi x}{c}, \ 0<x<c$$

from which it follows that

$$a_0=\frac{\theta_0}{c^3}\int_0^c (c^2-x^2)\ \mathrm{d}x=\tfrac{2}{3}\theta_0$$

$$a_n=\frac{2\theta_0}{c^3}\int_0^c (c^2-x^2)\cos\frac{n\pi x}{c}\ \mathrm{d}x.$$

A simple integration by parts shows that

$$a_n=\frac{4\theta_0}{n^2\pi^2}(-1)^{n+1}$$

so that we obtain finally the solution

$$\theta(x,\ t)=\tfrac{2}{3}\theta_0+\frac{4\theta_0}{\pi^2}\sum_{n=1}^{\infty}\frac{(-1)^{n+1}}{n^2}\cos\left(\frac{n\pi x}{c}\right)\mathrm{e}^{-n^2\pi^2kt/c^2}.$$

For further problems in the conduction of heat, the reader should try Nos. **6, 7, 8** at the end of this chapter.

5. VIBRATIONS OF BEAMS

We shall consider the transverse oscillations of a beam of uniform cross-section and of finite length l. In a free vibration in which y denotes the deflexion measured from the level of statical equilibrium, Newton's second law gives the equation of motion

$$m\frac{\partial^2 y}{\partial t^2}=\frac{\partial S}{\partial x} \tag{1}$$

where x is distance measured along the beam from one end O as origin, m is its mass per unit length and $S(x,\ t)$ is the shear. If we denote the sagging bending moment by $M(x,\ t)$, then

$$S=\frac{\partial M}{\partial x},\ \ M=-EI\frac{\partial^2 y}{\partial x^2} \tag{2}$$

where E denotes Young's modulus and I is the moment of inertia of its cross-section about the neutral axis. If we substitute from equations (2) into equation (1) we obtain the fourth order partial differential equation

$$\frac{\partial^4 y}{\partial x^4} + \frac{1}{k^2}\frac{\partial^2 y}{\partial t^2} = 0, \quad (k^2 = EI/m) \tag{3}$$

for the free vibrations of a uniform elastic beam.

If the vibrations are forced by an externally applied force $P(x, t)$, (including gravity if this is not to be neglected), this force must be added to the right-hand side of equation (1) and we obtain finally

$$\frac{\partial^4 y}{\partial x^4} + \frac{1}{k^2}\frac{\partial^2 y}{\partial t^2} = p(x, t) \tag{4}$$

where $p(x, t) = P(x, t)/EI$.

Considering first the case of free vibrations we put

$$y = Y(x)\cos(\omega t + \epsilon)$$

in equation (3) and find that the function $Y(x)$ satisfies the fourth order equation

$$\frac{d^4 Y}{dx^4} - q^4 Y = 0$$

where $q^4 = \omega^2/k^2$. The general solution of this equation is known to be

$$Y(x) = A \sinh qx + B \cosh qx + C \sin qx + D \cos qx. \tag{5}$$

The values of the constants A, B, C, D will depend on the boundary conditions we impose. We shall consider only the case of a beam freely hinged at its ends, i.e. $y = 0$, $M = 0$ at $x = 0$ and $x = l$. From the second of equations (2) this implies the boundary conditions $Y = Y'' = 0$ at $x = 0$ and at $x = l$ on the function $Y(x)$.

The conditions $Y(0) = Y''(0) = 0$ immediately give $B = D = 0$ while the conditions $Y(l) = Y''(l) = 0$ imply that

$$A \sinh ql = C \sin ql = 0.$$

Since, by the nature of the problem, $l \neq 0$ and hence

$\sinh q\, l \neq 0$, it follows that $A=0$. If $C=0$, the function $Y(x)$ is identically zero so that the only alternative left is that

$$\sin ql=0$$

which implies that $ql=n\pi$ $(n=1, 2, 3, \ldots)$ and hence that

$$\omega=\frac{\pi^2 k}{l^2}n^2, \ (n=1, 2, 3, \ldots). \tag{6}$$

For a free vibration satisfying the condition $\partial y/\partial t=0$ when $t=0$ we therefore have the basic solution

$$y_n(x, t)=b_n \sin \frac{n\pi x}{l} \cos \frac{n^2\pi^2 kt}{l^2}.$$

If $y=f(x)$ at $t=0$, then the appropriate solution of the equation (3) is

$$y(x, t)=\sum_{n=1}^{\infty} b_n \sin \frac{n\pi x}{l} \cos \frac{n^2\pi^2 kt}{l^2}, \ (0\leqslant x\leqslant l) \tag{7}$$

where

$$f(x)=\sum_{n=1}^{\infty} b_n \sin \frac{n\pi x}{l}, \ (0\leqslant x\leqslant l),$$

i.e.

$$b_n=\frac{2}{l}\int_0^l f(x) \sin \frac{n\pi x}{l}\, \mathrm{d}x. \tag{8}$$

On the other hand if $y=0$ when $t=0$ we take our basic solution to be

$$y_n(x, t)=B_n \sin \frac{n\pi x}{l} \sin \frac{n^2\pi^2 kt}{l^2}$$

so that if $\partial y/\partial t=g(x)$ at $t=0$, the solution of equation (3) is

$$y(x, t)=\sum_{n=1}^{\infty} B_n \sin \frac{n\pi x}{l} \sin \frac{n^2\pi^2 kt}{l^2} \tag{9}$$

where

$$g(x)=\frac{\pi^2 k}{l^2}\sum_{n=1}^{\infty} n^2 B_n \sin \frac{n\pi x}{l}$$

so that

$$B_n = \frac{2l}{\pi^2 k n^2} \int_0^l g(x) \sin \frac{n\pi x}{l} \, dx. \tag{10}$$

The use of equations (7) and (9) is illustrated by Problems **9** and **10** at the end of this chapter. Here we shall consider a more difficult problem involving forced vibrations:

Example 7. *The supports of a freely hinged elastic beam of length l are given a vertical displacement $a \cos 2\pi vt$. If initially the beam is at rest in the position $y = 0$ find its displacement at any subsequent time.*

If $y(x, t)$ is the deflexion at a point x from a support the acceleration of this point is

$$\frac{\partial^2 y}{\partial t^2} - 4\pi^2 v^2 a \cos 2\pi vt$$

and therefore the rate of change of momentum of an element of mass $m\delta x$ is

$$m\delta x \left(\frac{\partial^2 y}{\partial t^2} - 4\pi^2 v^2 a \cos 2\pi vt \right)$$

and this must be equated to the elastic restoring force

$$-EI \frac{\partial^4 y}{\partial x^4} \delta x.$$

Hence the equation governing y is

$$\frac{\partial^4 y}{\partial x^4} + \frac{1}{k^2} \frac{\partial^2 y}{\partial t^2} = \frac{4\pi^2 v^2 am}{EI} \cos 2\pi vt. \tag{11}$$

Now if we form the Fourier sine series of unity in the range $0 \leqslant x \leqslant l$ we find that

$$1 = \frac{4}{\pi} \sum_{r=1}^{\infty} \frac{1}{(2r-1)} \sin \frac{(2r-1)\pi x}{l}$$

so that equation (11) can be written in the form

$$\frac{\partial^4 y}{\partial x^4} + \frac{1}{k^2} \frac{\partial^2 y}{\partial t^2} = \frac{16\pi v^2 ma}{EI} \cos 2\pi vt \sum_{r=1}^{\infty} \frac{1}{(2r-1)} \sin \frac{(2r-1)\pi x}{l},$$

$$0 \leqslant x \leqslant l. \tag{12}$$

A particular integral of the equation

$$\frac{\partial^4 y}{\partial x^4} + \frac{1}{k^2} \frac{\partial^2 y}{\partial t^2} = \frac{1}{(2r-1)} \sin \frac{(2r-1)\pi x}{l} \cos 2\pi vt$$

is

$$\frac{1}{2r-1} \left\{ \frac{(2r-1)^4 \pi^4}{l^4} - \frac{4\pi^2 v^2}{k^2} \right\} \sin \frac{(2r-1)\pi x}{l} \cos 2\pi vt$$

so that

$$\frac{16\pi v^2 ma}{EI} \sum_{r=1}^{\infty} \frac{1}{(2r-1)} \left[\frac{(2r-1)^4 \pi^4}{l^4} - \frac{4\pi^2 v^2}{k^2} \right]^{-1} \sin \frac{(2r-1)\pi x}{l}$$

$$\cos 2\pi vt$$

is a particular integral of (12). Using the fact that, for any β_r the series

$$\sum_{r=1}^{\infty} \beta_r \sin \frac{(2r-1)\pi x}{l} \cos \frac{(2r-1)^2 \pi^2 kt}{l^2}$$

is a solution of the homogeneous equation (3) we see that the solution of (12) satisfying the conditions $y(x, 0) = \partial y(x, 0)/\partial t = 0$ is

$$y(x, t) =$$

$$\frac{16\pi v^2 ma}{EI} \sum_{r=1}^{\infty} \frac{\sin \dfrac{(2r-1)\pi x}{l}}{2r-1} \left[\frac{\cos(2\pi vt) - \cos \dfrac{(2r-1)^2 \pi^2 kt}{l^2}}{\dfrac{(2r-1)^4 \pi^4}{l^4} - \dfrac{4\pi^2 v^2}{k^2}} \right]$$

For a further example on the forced oscillations of an elastic beam the reader should attempt Problem **11** at the end of this chapter.

EXERCISES ON CHAPTER IV

1. Find the solution of the equation $\dfrac{\partial^2 y}{\partial x^2} = \dfrac{1}{c^2}\dfrac{\partial^2 y}{\partial t^2}$, where c is real and constant, which satisfies the conditions

    (i) $y=0$ at $x=0$ and at $x=l$, for all values of t,

    (ii) $y=0$ at $t=0$ for all values of x,

    (iii) $\dfrac{\partial y}{\partial t} = lx - x^2$, when $t=0$, for $0 < x < l$.

Show that when $x = \tfrac{1}{2}l$

$$y = \frac{8l^3}{c\pi^4} \sum_{r=1}^{\infty} (-1)^{r-1} \frac{\sin\{(2r-1)\pi ct/l\}}{(2r-1)^4}.$$

2. Find a solution $\psi(x, y)$ of Laplace's equation, valid inside the square
$$0 \leqslant x \leqslant a, \quad 0 \leqslant y \leqslant a,$$
given that ψ is zero everywhere on the boundary except on the segment $\tfrac{1}{3}a < x < \tfrac{2}{3}a$, $y=a$, where it has the value ψ_0.

Deduce that the value of ψ at the centre of the square is
$$\frac{2\psi_0}{\pi} \sum_{m=0}^{\infty} \frac{1}{2m+1} \sin\frac{(2m+1)\pi}{6} \operatorname{sech}\frac{(2m+1)\pi}{2}.$$

3. Find a solution ψ of Laplace's equation which satisfies the conditions

    (i) ψ remains finite as $y \to \infty$,

    (ii) $\partial\psi/\partial x = 0$ when $x=0$ and when $x=3$,

    (iii) when $y=0$, $\psi=x$ for $0 \leqslant x \leqslant 1$, $\psi=1$ for $1 \leqslant x \leqslant 2$ and $\psi=3-x$ for $2 \leqslant x \leqslant 3$.

4. Find the function $\psi(x, y)$ which satisfies Laplace's equation in the infinite strip $0 \leqslant x \leqslant 2l$, $y \geqslant 0$ and the boundary conditions

    (i) $\psi(0, y) = \psi(2l, y) = 0$;

    (ii) $\psi(x, 0) = \begin{cases} x^2/l, & 0 \leqslant x \leqslant l; \\ 2l-x, & l \leqslant x \leqslant 2l. \end{cases}$

    (iii) $\dfrac{\partial\psi(x, 0)}{\partial y} = 0$, $0 \leqslant x \leqslant 2l$.

5. Assuming that $V = R(r)\Theta(\theta)$, where R and Θ are respectively functions of r and θ alone, is a solution of the equation
$$\frac{\partial^2 V}{\partial r^2} + \frac{1}{r}\frac{\partial V}{\partial r} + \frac{1}{r^2}\frac{\partial^2 V}{\partial \theta^2} = 0,$$

show that
$$r^2\frac{d^2 R}{dr^2} + r\frac{dR}{dr} = p^2 R, \quad \frac{d^2\Theta}{d\theta^2} + p^2\Theta = 0,$$

where p is any real constant. Verify that the general solution of the first of these is $R = Ar^p + Br^{-p}$, where A and B are arbitrary constants.

EXERCISES ON CHAPTER IV

Show that the solution of the given equation which satisfies the conditions

(i) V remains finite as $r \to \infty$;

(ii) $V = 0$ when $\theta = 0$ and when $\theta = \pi$, for all values of r;

(iii) $V = \theta(\pi - \theta)$, when $r = a$, for $0 \leqslant \theta \leqslant \pi$

is

$$V(r, \theta) = \frac{8}{\pi} \sum_{n=1}^{\infty} \frac{\sin(2n-1)\theta}{(2n-1)^3} \left(\frac{a}{r}\right)^{2n-1}.$$

6. Show that the solution $\theta(x, t)$ of the linear diffusion equation which satisfies the conditions

(i) θ remains finite as $t \to \infty$,

(ii) $\dfrac{\partial \theta}{\partial x} = 0$ when $x = 0$ and $x = c$ for all values of t,

(iii) $\theta = \theta_0 \left(1 - \dfrac{x^2}{c^2}\right)$ for $0 < x < c$, when $t = 0$,

is

$$\theta = \tfrac{2}{3}\theta_0 - \frac{4\theta_0}{\pi^2} \sum_{n=1}^{\infty} \frac{(-1)^n}{n^2} e^{-kn^2\pi^2 t/c^2} \cos\left(\frac{n\pi x}{c}\right).$$

7. The temperature θ at depth x from one face of a conducting wall at time t satisfies the equation

$$\frac{\partial \theta}{\partial t} = k \frac{\partial^2 \theta}{\partial x^2}$$

where k is a positive constant. The face $x = 0$ is kept at zero temperature and the opposite face $x = l$ is perfectly insulated. If θ is finite for large values of t and $\theta = x$ at $t = 0$, show that when $t > 0$

$$\theta = \frac{2l}{\pi^2} \sum_{n=0}^{\infty} \frac{(-1)^n}{(n+\frac{1}{2})^2} e^{-(n+\frac{1}{2})^2 \pi^2 kt/l^2} \sin\left(\frac{(n+\frac{1}{2})\pi x}{l}\right).$$

8. The temperature θ at distance r from the centre of a sphere of radius a has radial symmetry and satisfies the equation

$$\frac{\partial(r\theta)}{\partial t} = k \frac{\partial^2(r\theta)}{\partial r^2}$$

where k is a positive constant. The surface of the sphere is kept at zero temperature and θ is everywhere finite. If θ is a given function $f(r)$ when $t = 0$ show that

$$\theta = \frac{1}{r} \sum_{n=1}^{\infty} A_n e^{-n^2 \pi^2 kt/a^2} \sin\frac{n\pi r}{a}$$

where

$$A_n = \frac{2}{a} \int_0^a r f(r) \sin\frac{n\pi r}{a}\, dr.$$

9. An elastic beam is deformed to the shape

$$y = \frac{4\epsilon}{l^2} x(l - x)$$

and released from rest. Show that in the subsequent motion

65

$$y = \frac{32\epsilon}{\pi^3} \sum_{r=1}^{\infty} \frac{1}{(2r-1)^3} \sin \frac{(2r-1)\pi x}{l} \cos \frac{(2r-1)^2 \pi^2 kt}{l^2}.$$

10. An elastic beam under no external forces and initially occupying the straight line $0 \leqslant x \leqslant l$ is freely hinged at its ends. At time $t = 0$ an impulse P is applied normal to the beam at the point $x = a$. Show that in the subsequent motion the transverse displacement of the beam is given by the equation

$$y(x, t) = \frac{2Pl}{\pi^2 km} \sum_{n=1}^{\infty} \frac{1}{n^2} \sin \frac{n\pi a}{l} \sin \frac{n\pi x}{l} \sin \frac{n^2 \pi^2 kt}{l^2}.$$

11. An elastic beam of length l, lying at rest in the position $y = 0$ is set in motion by the application of an alternating transverse force $F \cos 2\pi vt$ acting at the point $x = a$. Show that, in the subsequent motion, the transverse displacement is

$$\frac{2Fl^3}{\pi^4 EI} \sum_{r=1}^{\infty} \sin \frac{r\pi a}{l} \sin \frac{r\pi x}{l} \left\{ \frac{\cos(2\pi vt) - \cos(r^2 \pi^2 kt / l^2)}{r^4 - 4v^2 l^2 / \pi^2 k^2} \right\}.$$

ANSWERS TO EXERCISES

Chapter I:

1. $-\frac{1}{4}\pi + \frac{2}{\pi}\sum_{r=0}^{\infty}\frac{\cos(2r+1)x}{(2r+1)^2} - \sum_{n=1}^{\infty}\frac{2-(-1)^n}{n}\sin nx.$

3. $-\frac{8}{\pi}\sum_{n=1}^{\infty}\frac{n\sin 2nx}{(2n+1)(2n-1)}.$

4. $\frac{1}{\pi}\sinh\pi + \frac{2}{\pi}\sinh\pi\sum_{n=1}^{\infty}\frac{(-1)^n}{n^2+1}(\cos nx - n\sin nx).$

5. $\frac{2\lambda\sin\lambda\pi}{\pi}\sum_{n=1}^{\infty}\frac{(-1)^n}{\lambda^2-n^2}\cos nx + \frac{\sin\lambda\pi}{\lambda\pi}.$

Chapter II: **1, π.**

Chapter III:

2. $2\sum_{n=1}^{\infty}\frac{\sin nx}{n}.$

3. $\frac{4}{\pi}\sum_{r=1}^{\infty}\frac{\cos(2r-1)x}{(2r-1)^2}.$

6. (i) $2\sum_{n=1}^{\infty}(-1)^{n+1}\frac{\sin nx}{n}$; (ii) $2\sum_{n=1}^{\infty}(-1)^{n+1}\left(\frac{\pi^2}{n}-\frac{6}{n^3}\right)\sin nx.$

7. (i) $(x-2\pi)\cos x$; (ii) $(x-2\pi)\cos^2\frac{1}{2}x.$

8. $t-\frac{1}{4}\pi+\frac{1}{4}\pi\cos 2t,\ 0\leqslant t\leqslant\frac{1}{2}\pi,\ t-\frac{3}{4}\pi-\frac{1}{4}\pi\cos 2t,\ \frac{1}{2}\pi\leqslant t\leqslant\pi.$

9. $\frac{1}{2}+\frac{2}{\pi}\sum_{r=1}^{\infty}\frac{\sin(2r-1)x}{(2r-1)}.$

Chapter IV:

1. $\frac{8l^3}{c\pi^4}\sum_{r=1}^{\infty}\frac{\sin\dfrac{(2r-1)\pi ct}{l}\sin\dfrac{(2r-1)\pi x}{l}}{(2r-1)^4}.$

67

ANSWERS TO EXERCISES

2. $\dfrac{4\psi_0}{\pi} \displaystyle\sum_{r=1}^{\infty} \dfrac{(-1)^r \sin\dfrac{(2r+1)\pi}{6}}{(2r+1)\sinh(2r+1)\pi} \sin\dfrac{(2r+1)\pi x}{a} \sinh\dfrac{(2r+1)\pi y}{a}$.

3. $\dfrac{2}{3} - \dfrac{6}{\pi^2} \displaystyle\sum_{r=1}^{\infty} \dfrac{\sin^2(\frac{1}{3}r\pi)}{r^2} \cos\dfrac{2r\pi x}{3} e^{-2r\pi y/3}$.

4. $\dfrac{12l}{\pi^2} \displaystyle\sum_{r=2}^{\infty} \dfrac{(-1)^{r-1}}{(2r-1)^2} \sin\dfrac{(2r-1)\pi x}{2l} \cosh\dfrac{(2r-1)\pi y}{2l}$

$\qquad\qquad - \dfrac{2l}{\pi^3} \displaystyle\sum_{r=1}^{\infty} \dfrac{1-(-)^r}{r^3} \sin\dfrac{r\pi x}{2l} \cosh\dfrac{r\pi y}{2l}$

Index